MXAC

STALKER 2

Brenda Hampton Entertainment

P.O. Box 773

Bridgeton, MO 63044

Stalker 2

Copyright © 2020 Brenda Hampton

Printed in the United States of America

STALKER 2

A BRENDA HAMPTON NOVEL

FLASHBACK

Being in orange had become my new black and being in jail was no picnic. I wanted a do-over, but unfortunately for me, I wasn't going to get it. This was now my reality, and now, Brent and his wife, Lajuanna, had gotten their happily-ever-after. Me, on the other hand, I got nothing. Nothing but a hard-ass bed, terrible food and mediocre pussy sucking every now and then. The only good days came when Kendal and my grandbaby visited me. They'd only done so twice. She didn't have to, because Lord knows I had dropped the ball on her as a mother. I didn't see it then, but I sure as hell saw it now. I had time to reflect on many things. If I could turn back the hands of time, I most certainly would.

I sat in my orange jumpsuit, in the visiting quarters, waiting for Kendal and my grandson, Miguel, to come see me. He was adorable. It always brightened my day just to be able to hold him in my arms. I was sure that Kendal would, eventually, stop bringing him here to see me. But for now, I savored every little minute we'd had together.

Kendal was doing well, considering all that had happened. She had a job, she and her boyfriend, Micah, lived together and she even mentioned something about marrying him. I would miss that day too, because for the next thirty-five years, this place was my new home.

Feeling kind of bad today, I cracked a tiny smile as Kendal came into the room, carrying Miguel on her hip. He was playing with a toy and was already getting so big. I was hurting inside, but just so Kendal wouldn't notice, I did my best to hide my pain very well.

"Hello, Mama," she said as I stood to greet her. "How are you today?"

"I'm hanging in there." I reached out for my grandson, giving him a big kiss. "Muuuuah! Those cute little chubby cheeks are to die for. I love, love, love you!"

Miguel giggled as I sat him on my lap. I looked at Kendal. "I love you too, you know?"

"I do know that, and I wouldn't be here if I thought otherwise. You just made some real bad mistakes, Mama. Real bad, and nothing that anyone said or did could stop you from wanting Brent so badly."

"I know, but can we please not talk about him? I don't want to talk about him right now. I'd rather talk about what you've been up to, how you've been and what are your plans."

"I'm doing well. I wish I had a better job, but you already know how that is. I'm going to start looking for another one soon, but my search is going to be outside of St. Louis. That's what I came here to tell you. I'm planning on moving away from here, because the job market is slow. I can do better in a place like Atlanta, or possibly, North Carolina somewhere."

That wasn't good news to me. Kendal was all I had. If she went away, I was sure her visits would come to a halt. As would the money she'd been putting on my books.

"It's funny how I'm in a position where I have to count on you to take care of me. And even though your move disappoints me, please go live your life to the fullest. I'll be okay in here. Jus . . . just visit when you can and be sure to send me some pictures of my grandbaby. I want to see him grow up. Grow into a fine young man." I paused to look at Miguel who was busy with his toy. "Has your father seen him?"

Kendal shrugged. "Only one time, believe it or not. You know how he is. He doesn't have time for anyone, but himself. But that doesn't bother me anymore. It is what it is."

I reached over and touched Kendal's hand. "I'm so sorry, sweetheart. We both failed you, but I'm glad that you turned out to be an awesome and caring young lady. If that's because of Barbara then I have to thank her for that. She came through for me, when I didn't have my head on straight."

Kendal tried to spare my feelings. "Listen, Mama. I can't sit here and give Barbara all of the credit. You were a great mother, until Brent came along. Something about you changed, and while you don't want to talk about him, we have to. I don't want to push this under the rug any longer, and even though I made many attempts to get through to you before, you just never listened."

"Kendal, if I don't want to talk about him, I just don't want to talk about him. It's best that my memories of him stay buried. I hope you can understand that, can't you?"

"I do, but do me a favor, Mama. This may sting, but pick up Miguel for me. Look deep into his eyes, examine his features, especially his nose. Then tell me, who do you see? Who do you see when you look at him?"

Kendal's words made me nervous. I examined Miguel's features as she had asked. Even looked at his hands and feet, since his shoes were off. On the bottom of one of his feet was a birthmark. It was in the exact same spot as the one on Brent's foot. Miguel's eyes were similar. So was his nose and brows. My heart started to pound against my chest. When my eyes shifted to Kendal, she was nodding her head.

"You rarely questioned why I didn't like him. I had my reasons, but mainly because he had raped me one day while you were gone. I was afraid of him. That's why I left for good because you refused to get rid of him. Micah is the only one who knows the truth. I thought my baby was his, but when Miguel was born, Brent was written all over him. I was crushed, but Micah is helping me raise Miguel as his son. That's all he'll ever know. I ask you to keep this secret between us because I don't want any of us to hurt anymore because of that damn Brent Carson."

I was still. My dry lips stuck together. My eyes were without a blink, and my stomach was in a knot. I wanted to scream. Wanted to cry. Wanted to run out that door and go kill Brent, but I would only get so far. My emotions were about to boil over, so I gave Miguel back to Kendal. I stood and kissed them both.

"Goodbye, Kendal, and don't you ever come back here with your baby again. Thank you for sharing that with me. All I can say, again, is I'm sorry."

I walked away; didn't dare look back. And when the guard opened the door for me, I was escorted to my cell where I slowly laid on the cold, hard bed and looked at the ceiling. I closed my eyes and could hear Officer Eric Wayne yelling those five words at me, "*Is Brent Carson worth it?*"

Hell, no, he wasn't. But in thirty-five years, I would make him pay for all of this. Then again, revenge had never been mine. There was no question in my mind that Brent's mess would catch up with him and the punishment would be dire. People just needed to open their eyes and see who he really was.

CHAPTER ONE

3 months later

None of this was easy. As a matter of fact, it got real hard. The day I learned Brent Carson had raped my child changed everything. She now had his son. That didn't sit right with me, and if anyone thought I would go back to my shitty cell and pretend that I could brush off what Kendal had told me, they were confused. I wasn't that kind of woman. Never had been; never would be. At first, though, all I could do was cry my heart out and reflect on the past. I kept telling myself that something didn't add up, but then there was no disputing that two plus two equaled four. There was no other way to look at it. That bastard didn't deserve to be out there living it up with his wife who didn't seem to understand what kind of man she was married to. He didn't deserve to sleep peacefully at night, while I was laid up in here like this. I had to do something, and even though my revengeful mindset had gotten me in this place, all I could ask was one thing. What in the hell was I supposed to do? Sit here and rot? Pretend that everything was good and God would take care of Brent on His time? Please. That's not how I moved. The more I'd thought about it, the more I talked myself into somehow getting out of here and killing that bastard. He needed to die, now. Right now, he needed to pay. I wanted to burn that nigga alive and watch him scream like a bitch. I pictured myself chopping off his dick and shoving it down his throat. The thoughts in my head were downright sick, but I didn't care. I hated that man's guts, and less than a week after Kendal had left, I did what I knew best and plotted. Plotted a move to get the hell out of here. Yes, that's what I did, and as I sat patiently in the grimy motel I'd been in for two days now, I reminisced about how clever my escape plan was.

"Somebody needs to help her!" My roomy, Sade, yelled through the bars at the guard. "She's vomiting again. Puke is all over the place and it's starting to stink real bad in here!"

While Sade did what she had to do to get the guard's attention, I leaned over the toilet and held my stomach. For the fifth time this week, I'd pushed my fingers to the back of my throat, making myself regurgitate. Chunks of food from the horrible meals I'd eaten earlier were splattered over the toilet and floor. Some covered my mouth, and the foamy spit I kept adding to the mix made things look a whole lot worse than what it really was. The guard, Betty, casually walked up to the cell and tapped on the bar with her stick.

"Back up, Sade. Move back and stop all that damn yelling. Miss Abby will be just fine. She probably got the flu bug, and if you

12

nasty bitches would just learn to wash yo hands, you wouldn't get it. It'll be over within a few more days."

"No," Sade shouted. "This shit been going on for too long. The meds y'all gave her ain't working. I don't want her to die up in here. If she does, you know my uncle who's a well-known politician will hear about this."

"Screw your uncle. He's an asshole, and if he couldn't do anything to keep you out of this place, why in the heck do you think he'll care about her?"

As I stood up straight, I gagged and wiped across my wet, nasty mouth with the back of my hand. My eyes were narrow. There were bags underneath them from me losing sleep and crying so much.

"I wi . . . wish somebody would care," I said, stuttering. "I'm not well, and I honestly feel like I'm dying. Those meds are making me sicker. Please check with the warden to see if he made a decision about my visit to the hospital."

Sade's chest heaved in and out, as she looked at me with tears trapped in her eyes. Her performance was so spectacular; she needed to win an Oscar.

"Help her gotdamn-it! I can't believe you just standing there criticizing my fucking uncle. I swear I can't wait to talk to him."

Betty put her hand on her hip and barked back. "Screw you and your uncle. If you want to help, go clean up that mess she's made in there and chill the hell out. It's not that serious."

Sade grunted, and to my surprise, she reached through the bar and yanked Betty by her long, stringy hair. My eyes grew wide as Sade pounded Betty's head against the bars while blasting her. I was shocked because Sade's actions weren't part of the plan.

"Bitch, when I tell you to do something, you need to do it! How many times I gotta tell you she's dying in here? At least act like you give a damn!"

Betty struck Sade's hands with the stick, but she couldn't break her grip. It didn't take long for two other guards to show up and take control of the situation. The bars were unlocked, and within a matter of seconds, Sade was on the ground, shielding herself while being beaten and kicked.

"You're going to pay for this!" Betty said, stomping her. "How dare you put your hands on me! How dare you, you little cunt!"

After she punted Sade in her midsection, she rolled on her back and laughed out loud. This was no laughing matter to me, so I rushed over and tried to help.

"Stop hitting her! All she was trying to do was help me! Y'all wrong for this, and I'm telling—"

I couldn't even finish speaking, before one of the guards backed away from Sade and shoved me back. She shoved me so hard that I fell on the bed and hit my head against the wall. My head was spinning, but I had to stop them from beating on Sade. The only way to do that was to make this situation even more chaotic, so other decent guards would come. I screamed at the top of my lungs. I begged for help, and that caused some of the other female prisoners to speak up and more guards to rush towards our cell.

"What's going on in there?" a prisoner named Casey said. "It don't sound good, but are y'all alright?"

The last thing any of the guards wanted was a riot to start. A male guard who entered the cell pointed his finger at me while holding his stick up high. "Close your fucking mouth! Right now! You bitches are in a whole lot of trouble. I mean that shit!"

With a bruised eye and mouth full of blood, Sade spit on the floor. She kept laughing as they wrestled her out of the cell. "Do you, sis," she said to me then winked. "See you when I see you!"

Obviously, we both were heading to solitary. Or, so I thought. Instead, I was whisked away to an examination room where the same unprofessional nurse I'd seen earlier in the week checked me out again. With a nasty attitude, she was too close to me. The smell of her funky breath made me hold mine. Her pale skin appeared crusty and her whole uniform was filthy. I'd never known a nurse to treat patients with a dirty uniform on. Instead of it being white, it was gray. Probably because when I'd gotten here, another guard was in the room with her. I bet they'd been rolling around on the floor, and doing the nasty like everybody else around this place was sneaking and doing. She was pissed that my issue had interrupted them.

"Abby, go sit down over there and tell me what other symptoms you're having."

I sat in the chair, un-cuffed, with my head hanging low. My hair was scattered across my head and with fire-red eyes, I looked like a demon. My hands shook. I kept fidgeting like I was about to lose control.

"I . . . I don't know what's wrong with me." Fake tears cascaded down my face. I kept smacking them away. "It feels like I've been poisoned. I keep having hot flashes and I haven't slept in days. My head is banging, and it feels like somebody in there beating it like a drum. I . . . I can't explain it, but there's so much pain coming from the lower part of my neck, too. I don't know what's going on with me. All I know is I'm not ready to die. I don't want to die."

For the first time, I saw a hint of empathy in the nurse's eyes. She sucked in a deep breath, assuring me that I wasn't going to die.

"Just calm down and stop overreacting. I'll be back in a few minutes. I need to speak to someone about this."

The second she walked out the room, I rushed to my feet and hurried to find whatever I could use during my escape. The first thing I spotted was some scissors. I also saw some bandages and pills. I could hear the nurse talking to someone, so I knew I didn't have much time to gather much else. My eyes shifted across the room, and right when I saw the doorknob turn, I fell back in the chair and started coughing. I gagged as if I was choking on something and tightly held my stomach. The nurse looked at me, sighing again.

"Warden B hasn't made a decision yet, so all we can do is wait. Until then, be sure to take the meds when they're given to you and don't try anything foolish like you did earlier. So far, you haven't been in any trouble, Abby. Don't let Sade get you into trouble, okay? Just do what you're told and everything should be fine."

This whole system was fucked up. People on the outside didn't know how messed up it was. Criminal or not, I didn't deserve to be treated like this. I told these motherfuckers I was sick, and all they could tell me was to wait. Wait to die, I guess. I couldn't wait to get out of here. My plan was risky as ever, but at this point, I didn't have anything to lose.

"I'm not going to be fine," I said. "I need to go to the hospital, now. Whatever you can do to make that happen, I'd appreciate it."

The door opened, again. The same male guard who was in my cell entered.

"I'll take it from here," he said to the nurse. "And if you hear anything before morning, be sure to let me know. My shift doesn't end until seven."

The nurse nodded, as the guard moved in my direction with cuffs in his hand.

"Stand up," he ordered.

I slowly stood and was careful not to lose the scissors, bandages and pills. I had shoved them inside my pants. The guard cuffed me, but instead of escorting me back to my cell, he put me in solitary confinement. Ever since I had been in this place, I had never been in a grimy room like this. It was worse than my cell. I wasn't sure how long I would be here, but after the door was closed, I sat on the nasty floor with my back against the concrete wall. The tiny room was stuffy, and the smell of piss permeated *the air. It was so hot that I could already feel beads of sweat dotting my forehead. Only the strong could survive in an environment like this. I wasn't built for this shit, and someway or somehow, I needed to make my move fast. There was no question that I stood a better chance at escaping from a hospital than I did in here. In here, I would get caught. If so, I would probably have to stay in solitary confinement for months. I would go crazy for sure. Crazy like Sade who I now considered my best friend. She was the only person I trusted; I was so grateful to her for trying to help me do this. After I'd told her about what Brent had done, she was all in. She seemed to hate him more than I did, and she promised me that if I ever needed her, for anything, she would be there for me. I believed her. I believed that she had my back. I promised myself that if I was lucky enough to get out of here, I would do my best to make sure her uncle advised some of his connects to take another look at her case. This place wasn't for women, like us, who had been wronged by the men in our lives. They claimed to love us, but failed us in so many ways. Sade's man had proposed to her. The day before their wedding, she found out he had been having a sexual relationship with her brother. Her own damn brother! It was enough to send her over the edge. She stabbed both of them. Found them in bed together and sliced them with a knife. She didn't kill them, and from what she'd told me, it was self-defense.*

They tried to jump her; therefore, she had to defend herself. I wasn't there, but I definitely understood how she felt. Betrayed. Hurt. Alone and foolish for believing somebody loved you, as much as you loved them. Some men didn't get how important it was to mean what you say, especially men like Brent Carson who took me to my lowest point of my life and forced me to do everything I'd done to him.

As I lay on the floor in a fetal position, my eyes kept fluttering, but I couldn't sleep. I finally got up and kept pacing the floor, wondering if or when someone would come rescue me from being in a room that felt like it was closing in on me by the second. I was ready to throw in the towel, but what seemed like hours later, my prayers were answered. I was whisked away, again. This time, I was finally on my way to the hospital.

The vehicle I was in wasn't an ambulance, but there was a gurney, an escort detail and some medical equipment inside. I pretended to be sleep, while lying on my back. One of my hands was cuffed to a side rail, the other was free. With one eye opened, I examined the escort detail. He was a handsome, mocha chocolate man with long locs that mostly hung on one side of his head. The other side was nearly shaved off. He also had thick juicy lips and a pretty smile. I saw his smile widen, as he ignored me while conversing with someone over his cellphone. He laughed and mentioned something about, "later tonight." As he chit-chatted, I was too busy trying to figure out if I was going to make my move now or wait until I was at the hospital. Maybe I needed to act now, especially since he seemed occupied with the caller. I also had to deal with the person driving the vehicle. I wasn't sure if there were one or two people in the front. Either way, something told me to act now.

I groaned like I was in pain and swayed my head from side-to-side. "Where . . . where am I?" I questioned. "I feel dizzy."

"I'll call you back," the escort said to the caller. "Around nine or ten."

He tucked the phone in his pocket and leaned over me. "You're on your way to the hospital. The meds are probably making you dizzy, but we should arrive at the hospital in about fifteen or twenty minutes."

He was so nice. I hated to play games with him like this, and I surely hoped I wouldn't have to kill him. In order for me to get out of this situation, I either had to use the scissors that were tucked away in my pants to stab him or attempt to get his gun. Doing that seemed much easier, especially since one of my hands was free.

"Twenty minutes seem like a long time. I feel like I need to vomit again. My stomach hurts and—"

I paused and swallowed hard. As if he really cared for me, he hurried to put on gloves and reached for a plastic bag.

"Use this," he said, moving closer to me. My eyes were fixated on the gun on his side. It was right there for the taking.

I quickly sat up and coughed into the bag. Trying to avoid my germs, he turned his head to the side and slightly frowned. My heart raced as I looked at his gun, again, trying to contemplate if the timing was right. Deep down, I felt it was. He was distracted by my coughs, and right when he turned his head away from me a little bit more, that's when I snatched his gun from the holster. He tried to back up and overpower me, but by then I had the gun aimed right at his chest.

"Back the fuck up and hands up," I said with a twitching eye. He had to know that I was serious about harming him, even though I wouldn't hurt a fly. Then again, maybe Brent. That was it. Just him, and no one else, if I could help it.

"What's going on back there?" the driver shouted. "Drew, are you au'ight?"

"No he's not," I shouted back. "And he's not going to be okay, if you don't listen to me."

"Drew!" the driver said again. Drew eased his hands up, while gazing at the gun that trembled in my hand.

"Listen to what she says," he replied to the driver. "She has my gun, so please listen, alright?"

The driver didn't respond. I figured he was the only one else in the vehicle, because no one else said anything.

"Do not go to the hospital," I said. "Drive to a secluded area and park this vehicle. If you do not listen to me, I swear I'm going to splatter Drew's brains all over back here and kill yo ass too."

The driver still didn't respond, but the vehicle was moving. I glared at Drew with a hard stare and nudged my head toward the driver. "Tell him to listen to me. Tell him now or we can end this right here."

For whatever reason, Drew seemed relaxed. He didn't seem to fear me. A part of me knew he could probably overpower me and get the gun away from me. I guess he didn't want to take any chances. He did exactly what I'd asked, and begged the driver to do the right thing.

"Man, I want to see my girls later. I know you want to see your son, too, so do what she says."

At first there was silence. Then, the driver spoke up again. "Yeah, whatever. But just remember that this shit is on you, nigga. Not on me."

"Got it," Drew said. "This is on me and I'll take responsibility for it."

The vehicle sped up, and as Drew almost lost his balance, I poked the gun against his chest.

"Be still. Remove the cuffs and stop looking at me. Why are you looking at me anyway? Like you know me or something."

"I just don't understand how a woman as beautiful as you are can find yourself caught up in—"

"Yeah, yeah, yeah, nigga, whatever. I've heard it all before, so stop with the small talk. Remove the cuffs, before I silence your whack ass."

He swallowed and reached for the keys to remove the cuffs. While still aiming the gun at him, I hurried off the gurney and tried to keep my balance while standing up.

"Slow down," I yelled to the driver. "And if you crash before we reach our destination, you're a dead man."

"I don't know who you think you are, but you'd better be glad my partner and me are good friends. Just shut the hell up. I'mma park this bitch in a few more minutes."

I didn't say a word. Just kept looking at Drew who stared at me with his hooded eyes. I wondered what he was thinking. I could tell he was plotting to come for me. Time wasn't on my side. In a matter of seconds, this situation could turn ugly. He could wrestle with me and have this gun back in his hands. I would then be on my way back to that shitty jail cell, with ten or twenty more years added to my sentence. Thinking about it made me sick. Thoughts of Brent being free made me sick. Revenge was that serious for me, and if Drew or anybody else stood in the way of me getting to that bastard, I had to do what was necessary.

The vehicle came to a halt. Seconds later, the driver spoke up.

"Get out," he said in a nasty tone. "Hurry the fuck up, before I call for back up."

I didn't have time to argue with him. Instead, I nudged my head and ordered Drew to unlock the secured back doors. In no rush, he casually unlocked the doors and opened one side wide so I could get out.

"Go," he said. "But can I have my gun back?"

"Hell no, because I'mma need it. Back away from the door and be sure to tell ol' boy to drive off fast, once I'm out."

I jumped down from the vehicle, noticing that I was in an alley. The stench of trash breeze through the air, two dogs were lurking to the left of me, and a homeless man was standing by a door, trying to be nosy. As I proceeded to run off, Drew grabbed my arm and surprised the hell out of me.

"I'll be sure to tell Sade you made it," he said in a whisper. "Take this and don't look back."

He slapped a hundred dollar bill in my hand. I was at a loss for words. I knew this was too easy, and unfortunately, I didn't have time to ask him any questions. He released my arm and shut the door. Seconds later, the truck sped away. I watched it zoom down the alley, and as for me, I was just happy to be . . . FREE.

CHAPTER TWO

It felt good to be out of the motel and inhaling fresh air that truly gave me life. I had missed this. Missed my freedom, and after nearly one year in that dump, I'd had enough. Today was a new day. A part of me was afraid that I would get caught, especially since I assumed details of my escape had been broadcasted on the news. I avoided watching TV, didn't associate with anyone and kept watching my back. The first thing I needed was money. I didn't have much, and if it wasn't for Drew slapping a hundred bucks in my hand, I wouldn't have been able to pay for the motel or jeans and oversized t-shirt I'd gotten from a lady who was near the motel selling merchandise. She was right on time, and I was able to get some body cleansing products from her, too.

I definitely wanted to know more about Drew's involvement in all of this. After the way Officer Eric Wayne had lied to me, I didn't trust anyone. He was another one on my shit list. That bastard had set me up and worked behind the scenes with Brent and his wife to bring me down. Eric was one of the main reasons I was in jail. He would be dealt with, but not before I dealt with Brent Carson.

Until then, I had to find somebody in St. Louis who could help me look different. Not just throw some makeup on me or redo my hairstyle, but I needed to find someone who specialized in cosmetic surgery. My facial structure had to change a bit, and since men always adored my eyes, I wanted to change them to a cattish gray. From being under so much stress and not eating much, my curves were there, but not as much as they used to be. I had a very slender frame with a plump backside. I'd never had big breasts, but maybe it was time to change that. I envisioned all the things I could have done to make myself look different, but those things couldn't happen without money. I wasn't sure if turning to my ex-husband Malik for help was the right move or not. He definitely had the money I needed, but the last time I saw him things didn't go well. I told him Kendal was pregnant. With him being her father, I thought he'd be happy and the news would be a turning point for us. Instead, he fussed about not wanting to be a grandfather at such a young age and accused me of being a bad parent. The more I'd thought about how bad things had gone that day, I decided to scratch him from the list and add him to my shit list. Just maybe I'd get around to dealing with him, too.

The only other people I thought about contacting were Kendal, of course, and possibly a gay guy named Jeff who knew Brent rather well. He was the one who basically told me Brent wasn't shit and was still married to Lajuanna. Since Jeff's whole face had been made over, I figured he would know where I could have my makeover done. I just wasn't sure if he would be able to keep seeing me a secret. Nobody could know—maybe, not even Kendal. Lord knows I wanted to see her and my grandbaby, but the last time we spoke, she was looking forward to moving away from St. Louis. I encouraged her to start a new life elsewhere. I wanted her to leave behind all the mess I had brought to her life. Hopefully, Kendal and Micah were happy together. That was my wish. She didn't need me out here causing any problems for her. At that moment, I decided not to contact her at all. Instead, I asked a lady if I could use her phone, called Uber and had the driver take me to Jeff's beauty shop on Delmar Avenue in the St. Louis Loop. The second I walked through the door, I heard his loud mouth. His back was to me; he was talking to one of his customers, as she sat in a chair.

"Look, I don't mind doing your hair, but some of y'all need to wash that shit, before you come here. Ain't nothing pretty about trying to work with dirty ass hair. You can be mad at me all you want, but you know I always tell it like it is."

Of course he did. I couldn't believe his business was thriving and customer base was thick. Jeff was too much, and as he stood there in high heels, wearing a flowered silk robe while styling his customer's hair, all I could do was shake my head.

"Can I help you?" one of the other stylists asked.

Before I could respond, Jeff swung around to look at me. I guess he didn't recognize me, because he rolled his eyes and turned back around to his customer.

"As I was saying," he paused and swung around again. This time, his eyes grew wide. He kept blinking, causing his long lashes to flutter.

"Bioootch, are you serious? Is that really you, Sweet Pea?"

Not wanting to bring too much attention to myself, I nodded and quickly walked his way. Slightly nervous, I popped my knuckles and fidgeted.

"Can we, uh, talk somewhere in private for a few minutes?"

With red matte lipstick on, Jeff pressed his lips together, while searching me up and down with his eyes. "Sure we can. I almost didn't recognize you, and why are you so damn bony? I heard about . . ."

I quickly cut him off. "Jeff, please. We need to talk in private."

"Okay, sugga. Get you some of those chocolates over there and grab a glass of wine. My office is down the hall, last door on the right. Give me ten minutes. I should be done with this nasty heifer's hair by then."

Jeff and a few other people laughed. The woman in the chair just threw her hand back, as if she didn't even care about how obnoxious he was. I minded my own business, and after snatching up two chocolate covered strawberries, I headed to Jeff's office.

I had to admit that his whole shop was fabulous. His office had a white velvet sectional in it, with a circular furry rug in the center of the room. His desk was made of glass, and there was an orange wingback chair behind it. Black-and-white photos of Beyoncé, Janet Jackson, Rihanna and Ciara covered the walls. He had very expensive taste, and all the glitz and glam must've cost him a fortune. I took a seat on the plush sectional and waited for him to join me. Almost twenty minutes later, he came busting through the door, swishing his hips like he was getting ready to walk the runway. His robe blew behind him, and with six-inch heels on, Jeff was quite the queen. He sat on the sectional next to me and crossed his legs.

"Sweet Pea, I must say that I am sooooo shocked to see you. Last I heard, yo crazy ass was in jail on some dumb, obsessive shit with Brent. Everybody was talking about it. I was shook that you fucked up yo life for a loser like that. You know that man ain't right."

His words made me feel real stupid. The somber look on my face said it all. "I know I messed up, and I can't deny that I made some horrible mistakes."

Jeff cocked his head back. "Mistakes? Bitch, you flew out of the cuckoo's nest for that nigga. He told you he didn't want you. You just flat out went crazy and lost yo damn mind. That dick wasn't even all that big or good. Don't ask me how I know, because if you do, I will have to tell you I had that shit in my mouth before and it didn't even taste right."

Without even knowing it, Jeff hit me with another blow to my stomach. I wanted to get up and walk out, but I couldn't. I swallowed the lump in my throat and sucked in a deep breath. Jeff could tell I was frustrated.

"Don't tell me you still get worked up when people talk about that nigga. You look like you about to cry. If you are, please don't do it around me. I don't feel sorry for women who let men dog the shit out of them and then go to jail for—" Jeff paused and clapped his hands. "Please tell me why you're here? I thought you were in jail for twenty, thirty or forty-something years. How did you get out?"

"I'll tell you everything, but more than anything, I need your help. You can't tell anyone I was here and you have to promise me that you won't tell Brent, or his wife, that you saw me."

"First of all, bitch, I don't know you like that. I saw you a few times when you were dating Brent and that's it. So for you to sit there and ask me to make you any promises is foul. I don't commit to promises, and if the police come here looking for you, I'm snitching. You'll never hear about a fine, pretty bitch like me in jail over no messy shit. That ain't me. You've come to the wrong place, if you think it is."

Jeff's words crushed my plans. Maybe coming here was a big mistake, but I honestly had nowhere else to turn.

"Okay, no promises or nothing. Just listen and let me explain what really happened between me and Brent. Yes, I made some mistakes, but people don't know the whole truth. The truth is—"

"The truth is you were desperate, lonely and downright stupid. Let's get that out of the way first, before you go on."

"I agree. Yes, I was and after I found out he raped my daughter, I might be so much more than that."

Jeff sat back and pursed his lips. "Go ahead. I'm listening."

For the next hour or so, I gave Jeff the scoop about what happened the day I was arrested. I explained how Officer Eric Wayne had played me, by telling me he'd killed Brent and Lajuanna. I also told Jeff about Brent raping Kendal and about my grandchild that was his. Jeff shook his head the whole time, especially when I told him how I'd escaped.

"See, you gon' have me as an accessory to all of this mess. I don't want no parts of it, Sweet Pea, and I'm sorry all of this has happened to you and your daughter."

"Then please help me. Hook me up with your cosmetic surgeon and . . . and can I please borrow some money?"

Jeff hopped up and tightened the strap on his robe. "Whoop, there it is. I knew it was something. It all circles back to money. Money that I don't have, and if I did, what makes you think I would give it to you?"

"Because, I know you like me Jeff. The day we met, we clicked. Deep down, you know all of this isn't my fault. I was tricked. We've all been tricked before and I know you understand what that feels like."

Jeff rolled his eyes. He sighed and sat back on the sectional. "Yeah, I've been tricked a few times, too, but bitch I ain't never done no stupid crap like you did. All you gon' do is get yourself in more trouble." He clapped his hands together to make his point. "Why, why, why don't you just leave that man alone and go somewhere and chill. What's done is done. Let it be and take responsibility for your actions. You fucked up, too. I've yet to hear you say that this is on you as well."

"Trust me, it is. I know it is, but I just can't let Brent get away with this. I can't Jeff. He needs to pay for my pain, right here and now."

"Pay for it how? Are you going to kill him and get yourself in more trouble? Kill Lajuanna? Just what are you going to do, Abby? I'm confused, because haven't we been here before?"

Jeff's words made me think. Yes, I wanted Brent dead. I wanted to torture and kill him with my own hands. I wanted him to see me free and fear me in every way possible. I just couldn't answer Jeff's questions. He kept asking, but I sat there thinking about my freedom, while trying to decide what I really wanted.

"Yeah, that's what I thought. You don't want to kill that man. After everything he did, you still love him. I can't believe you still have feelings for him. What is it gon' take, Sweet Pea, for you to rid yourself of that fool?"

I lowered my head, and then lifted it to look at him with seriousness in my eyes. "Listen, okay? There is not an ounce of love left in my body for that man. I hate his guts, but as much as I hate him, I don't know if killing him is the right thing to do yet.

Maybe I should just have my surgery done and let all of this go. I'm as free as I can be now. That's a good thing, right?"

"It damn sure is. And it's good to hear you talking like you got some sense. If that's what you decide, I'll hook you up with my surgeon and give you some cash. But as soon as you make some dough, I want my shit back. Got it?"

I smiled and felt relieved. It was good that someone was willing to help me. I just wasn't quite sure yet if I was willing to help myself by staying away from Brent Carson.

CHAPTER THREE

The following day, Jeff took me to Dr. Shekah, a cosmetic surgeon he had known for years. I was kind of skeptical because his office wasn't in a regular doctor's office like I had hoped. Instead, it was in a small brick building that looked like numerous, spacious lofts were inside. There was something fishy going on for sure, but Jeff assured me that Dr. Shekah was the right man for the job.

"You need to calm yo ass down," Jeff said, sitting next to me as I bit my nails. "I told you I would take care of you. If you don't trust me, then walk yo ass out that door right now and get arrested."

"It's okay," Dr. Shekah said with a wide smile on his face. He reminded me of Dr. Oz, with full Botox on display. He touched my leg as I sat on the examination table. "I will take care of you for sure. What you want sounds simple, but I can make you look like Kim Kardashian, Jennifer Lopez or Kylie Jenner. Many of my patients—"

"Excuse me, but don't nobody wanna look like them hoes," Jeff snapped. "This is a beautiful black woman right here. All she needs to be is tweaked. Let's talk about Halle Berry, Kerry

Washington, Meagan Good or some other fine black bitches you can replicate."

Dr. Shekah cleared his throat. "I'm sorry. I didn't mean to offend anyone."

"Well, you did," Jeff snapped again and rolled his eyes. "I'm in here bragging about how good you are, and you trying to get my Sweet Pea to look like a damn snow bunny. Get the fuck outta here."

While I understood Jeff's point, I had to intervene so this wouldn't get out of hand. "Listen, Doc, I told you what I wanted. No ass injections, no puffy lips and no Botox. Just work with my facial structure, heighten my cheekbones, raise my brows, color my eyes and I'll need to have something done to my hair. I'm interested in breast implants, too. Might as well get those done. It's something I always wanted."

Jeff turned to Dr. Shekah again. "Before you do any of this, let me know how much it's going to set me back. She talking about what she wants, but let's be clear. Sweet Pea ain't got no money. I'm the one paying for this."

Dr. Shekah said he would make sure the price was right. He left the room, and that's when Jeff inquired about my plans again.

"I know you had time to get some rest last night and think about what you gon' do. Have you decided to leave St. Louis, go find your daughter or what?"

"I really don't know yet. I didn't get any sleep last night. All I did was toss and turn. I have so much on my mind. Not only was I thinking about Brent and Kendal, but I told Sade that if I made it out, I would do what I could to get her out. Her uncle is Governor Johnson. I know he can help her. He has to, but I don't know how to confront him."

"You know, for you to do all this crazy crap and scheming like you do, you're not that bright. Anybody knows that when you want a politician to do something, all you have to do is convince them with money, sex and lies. I'm sure you'll figure it out. I don't know who this Sade person is, but it seems like she did a lot to help you. Don't turn your back on her. Just do what you can to help her, like she helped you."

Dr. Shekah came back into the room and showed Jeff the bill. He slapped his hand on his forehead, pretending to faint. "Chile, this is too much. You gon' owe me big time, and just so you know, I kill folks who don't return my money."

I thought the price was a bit much, but was happy he was willing to pay it. A smirk was on my face; I promised him I would repay every single dime. "If not me, Brent will. How about that?"

"How about you get yo tail in that operation room, before I change my mind? Brent is gon' be the death of you, Sweet Pea. You'd better leave his ass alone."

I didn't say one word. Jeff didn't know me well at all. Brent may have won the first round, but the more I'd thought about it, there wasn't a chance in hell I would let him win again. Thankfully, it was time for my surgery. I was looking forward to seeing the new me.

My whole body was sore. It felt like I'd been beat down. I couldn't even move—could barely open my eyes. When I did, my vision was blurred. I could see Dr. Shekah talking to someone, but I couldn't make out what he was saying. My face was wrapped with bandages. Breasts were too; they felt real tight. I needed something for the pain I'd felt, but my lips were so stiff I couldn't even speak. I did, however, release a soft moan. That's when Dr. Shekah, along with a very beautiful woman next to him, turned to face me. Smiles were on both of their faces.

"You're finally awake," Dr. Shekah said, moving closer to me. "You're probably feeling a little pain, but I'm going to give you something for it soon. I want you to know that your surgery went very well. You look fabulous, even more beautiful than you were before. I know you're going to be pleased, right Gina?"

Gina moved closer and touched my hand. "Right. I assisted Dr. Shekah today. You were the perfect patient. I can't wait for you to see how amazing you look."

I couldn't wait to see the new me either. But when I lifted my hand to touch the bandage on my face, Dr. Shekah stopped me.

"Not just yet. Allow the swelling to go down for a couple of days, and then I'll remove the bandages. I'll be able to show you your breasts implants later today. Those turned out great! Not too big, not too small. Just right and so much better than those little tits you had before."

He giggled, but I didn't see anything funny. I wanted to see how I looked. I was nervous about this, and I hoped Jeff was still around. He would tell me the truth for sure.

"Are you in a little or a lot of pain?" Dr. Shekah asked.

I nodded fast, signaling that I was in a lot of pain. He gave me some pain medicine through an IV, and a few minutes later, I started to fade again.

What seemed like many hours later, maybe even another day, I woke up again. Much of the pain had subsided. I was able to sit up a little. I looked down and could see the mountains on my chest. They appeared firm. For the moment, I was satisfied, but was eager to see my face. My eyes examined the room for a mirror, but I didn't see one. I kept patting the bandages on my face, trying to see if I could get a feel for how it had been restructured. My lips felt puffy, and that was unfortunate because I hadn't told Dr. Shekah to reconstruct them in any way. Right as I was touching them, Dr. Shekah and Jeff came into the room. Jeff had a blank expression on his face that made me real nervous. Dr. Shekah, however, still had glee in his eyes.

"Is something wrong?" I asked Jeff.

He shrugged and gazed at me with a frown. "I don't know yet. I'll tell you my thoughts when I see all of you."

His response frustrated me. I was ready to see my face now. The anticipation was killing me. I couldn't wait another day or two.

"Dr. Shekah, can you please remove the bandages? I need to see how I look right now."

Dr. Shekah's smile vanished. "I don't recommend that you see your face right now. Please give it a few more days. The swelling is going to frighten you. You won't have a clear picture of what you actually look like."

I rejected his recommendation. "I understand all of that and I'll consider everything you said. But I need to see my face right now. Please remove the bandages or I'll remove them myself."

He sighed and looked at Jeff.

"What in the hell are you looking at me for? I want to see her face, too. If you done fucked her up, now is the time to let us know what's up. Don't wait until the bandages come off. It might be too late by then, and just so you know, Abby can fight."

Dr. Shekah waved me off. He appeared frustrated with both of us, but I didn't care. "At least let me show you your breasts first. Those—"

"No," I shouted as loud as I could. My throat ached when I did it. I made it clear that I wanted to see my face. "Now, if you don't mind. Please let me see it now."

Dr. Shekah gave in. He prepped a small table beside me and slowly started to cut the bandages away from my face. Jeff stood with a trembling hand covering his mouth. At one point, he turned his back to me and put his hands together to pray.

"Lord, please forgive me. What have I done by recommending a doctor without a license?"

At that point, I grabbed Dr. Shekah's hand and threatened him through clenched teeth. "You better not have messed up my face. I swear to God I'm going to—"

He snatched his arm away from my grip. "Please calm down. I don't know what Jeff's problem is. He hasn't seen anything yet. Maybe its best if he waits in the hallway."

"Nope, I'm staying right here," Jeff said, rolling his neck around. "I need to see her face, because if you done fucked her up, I want my money back. Please proceed."

Dr. Shekah continued. And as more bandages were removed, Jeff kept acting up. He was shaking his head, sighing, releasing deep breaths and even had tears in his eyes. When all of the bandages were removed, he just stood there looking at me without a blink.

"What?" I questioned. My heart thumped hard against my chest. I was scared. Scared that the doctor had messed up. "How does my face look? Tell me and stop staring at me like that."

Jeff moved closer, squinting as he inspected my face. "You're black, you're poor, you're ugly, you're a woman, you're nothing, Celie. You also may be the prettiest bitch I done ever seen. I think you might like this. You look like what's her face? Uh, Nicole Murphy. Eddie Murphy's baby's mama."

I was afraid to smile, even though I thought she was pretty. I also didn't know if he was joking with me or not, especially since my skin color was slightly browner than hers was.

"Don't play, Jeff."

"Get that heifer a mirror, please. She won't approve of the swelling, but I can envision what's beyond it."

44

Dr. Shekah reached for a round mirror and held it in his hand. "Again, please ignore the swelling. Also, I know you didn't want anything done to your lips, but during surgery I decided to make them a little more plush to go with the new structure of your face. It's slightly slimmer and I was able to get rid of some of your lines and dark spots."

Without hesitation, I snatched the mirror from Dr. Shekah's hand. At first look, I gasped and felt unsure. I looked like a completely different woman. The changes he'd done made me look like someone else for sure. That alone scared me. The swelling was bad, but I could honestly say that he'd done a good job. My lips were thicker than I wanted, and once I put in gray contact lenses, that would be all she wrote. Jeff was right. My face, as well as my body, resembled Nicole's. I wanted my hair shorter, and I liked the way she styled hers. The only thing I didn't like was my somewhat pointed nose. It still looked the same as before, but I wasn't going to let Dr. Shekah do anything else to me.

"So, what do you think?" Dr. Shekah asked.

I nodded and continued to look at my face in the mirror. "I think this will work. I really do. Thank you for being patient with me and Jeff."

Jeff threw his hand back and didn't have much else to say. Dr. Shekah showed me my boobs; those were on point, too. Now all I had to do was wait until the swelling went down. After that, it was time to get this show on the road.

CHAPTER FOUR

Due to my surgery, I was down for nearly three weeks. It took a minute for my new look to come together like I wanted it to, and even though I still didn't feel one-hundred percent yet, I couldn't wait much longer to get to Brent. During my down time, Jeff was the bomb. He had done so much for me, and after hours of talking to him about what I'd finally decided to do, he understood why I couldn't let this go. He was willing to help me under two conditions. One was I had to make sure my actions didn't incriminate him in any way. Two was he wanted me to agree that his assistance was a loan that needed to be paid back with interest. While he understood I needed a place to stay, vehicle, cellphone and even a little cash, he just didn't trust me. That's why I had to sign a contract to pay everything back and then some. I didn't mind, especially since I didn't have anywhere else to turn. I intended to pay him back for all of it, and if I didn't, the contract terms revolved around me losing my life.

The one-bedroom apartment Jeff hooked me up with was on the Southside of St. Louis, and he let me use his 2009 Volkswagen Jetta for transportation. I wasn't picky at all and was more appreciative than anything. I assumed that Jeff felt sorry for me. Then again, he talked to me more about the down-low relationship he'd had with Brent. Jeff despised him a lot, and like me, he felt like Brent had a side to him that was problematic in so many ways. He admitted that his connection to Brent was a one way thing, where Brent used him whenever he wanted an "out of this world" blowjob. I'd thought about all the times I'd given him head—I guess it was never good enough. What about Lajuanna? Was she not good enough? I couldn't believe how I'd fallen head over heels for him. Every day, I beat myself up for being such a fool.

Earlier that day, I drove around, trying to find Brent. Jeff wasn't much help. He thought, like I did, that Brent and Lajuanna still lived in the same house. Unfortunately, they didn't. They had moved. I wasn't sure if they'd left St. Louis and relocated somewhere else. In order to find out, I decided to go back to the last place he was employed. I had been employed there, too, but the new receptionist at the desk told me Brent no longer worked there.

"I'm an old friend of his from college," I said. "I'm in town on business and I thought I could find him here. This is where he told me he worked."

"He worked here for a while," she politely said. "But then he went back to teaching again. I'm not sure where, but maybe my boss knows. Let me check with him."

As the receptionist stepped away from her desk, I figured she was going to ask Chris if he knew where Brent worked. Chris and I had an interesting relationship, while I worked here. He'd had a crush on me, and there were times when he'd said things that were considered sexual harassment. The only reason I'd worked here was to get close to Brent. He pretended that he wanted to hook up with me again, but in reality he was setting me up.

I stood there wondering if when Chris saw me again, would he notice me. My voice hadn't really changed, but I'd practiced a lot, trying to make it sound slightly different.

"Who wants to know about Brent?" Chris said as he walked into the lobby.

I stood with my wavy hair slicked on my head and hoop earrings dangling from my ears. My gray eyes were in full effect, and my thick lips were covered with a soft nude gloss. My frame was thin, but I had just enough curve in my hips to stop any man in his tracks. The breasts implants enhanced my look, and without saying one word, Chris's eyes implied he was hooked. Again.

"I forgot what she said her name was," the receptionist said. "But she's looking for Brent Carson. I thought you might know where he works. He's teaching somewhere, right?"

Chris couldn't stop drooling as he looked at me. He wiped the corner of his mouth, before dipping his hands into his pockets. He was a nerdy white man. I wasn't sure if I could use his services after today or not. We'd have to see.

"My name is Viola Cummings. I knew Brent in college, and the last time I reached out to him on social media, he told me he worked here. Said I should stop by, if or when I came to St. Louis."

"I see," Chris said, observing me. I wasn't sure if he recognized me or not, especially from the way he kept staring. "I'm not sure how long ago he told you that, but he hasn't worked here in quite a while. He's teaching at a high school in the North County area. In the Hazelwood district, I think. I'm not sure which one, but if I find out, I can always call and let you know, if you leave a number where I can reach you."

I had no intentions of giving him my phone number. Chris was still being Chris. I didn't want to be bothered with him, and since there weren't many high schools in the North County area, I figured it wouldn't be hard to track Brent down.

"I don't think leaving my contact information will be necessary. Thanks for the information, though. Have a nice day and I appreciate your time."

I pivoted to walk away. By the time I reached the door, Chris had already rushed up to open it for me.

"No problem, Viola. Stop by any time. I'm always here from eight in the morning, until nine at night."

I smiled and hurried to get away from that creep. Maybe I could trick him into giving me some money. If not that, I had no use for him. I left without saying anything else to him. Brent was the only person on my mind. Now all I had to do was find out which high school he worked at. I sat in my car, making phone calls. The third school I called, which was Hazelwood High School, the receptionist asked if I would like to leave a message for Mr. Carson, the school's counselor.

"As a matter of fact, I would. Please transfer me to his voicemail."

As soon as she transferred the call, I listened to his deep, masculine voice on the recorder. Hearing his voice gave me chills. It also angered me and caused my eye to twitch. When the beep came, I didn't quite know what to say. I didn't want to reveal myself in any way, but I decided to toy with him.

"Mr. Carson, this is Jameca's mother, Francine. She's been having some issues at school and I would like to have a discussion with you about her behavior. If you can, please return my call. I'm sure you'll be able to help get her on the right track. She always speaks so highly of you."

I left a number for him to call me back. By the time he did, I was already parked in front of the school. I answered the call in the sweetest voice possible.

"I'm trying to reach Francine," he said. "Not sure what the last name is, because—"

"It doesn't matter what my last name is. I would like to speak to you about my daughter."

"I'm perfectly fine with that, but if you don't mind telling me who your daughter is, I'll be able to assist you. There are several students here named Jameca. I can't recall all of them, but what's her last name?"

"It's whatever you want it to be."

I ended the call and laughed. I was excited to be this close to him again, and it was just a matter of time before we were face-to-face. I looked into the rearview mirror, shined my lips with more gloss, bumped up my hair a little and buttoned my suit jacket when I exited the car. My tan suit was accessorized with gold jewelry, and with leopard-print heels on, I was killing it. With

Drew's gun in my purse, I strutted to the main entrance like I had a million bucks. Unfortunately, I was immediately stopped by security.

"Good afternoon, Ma'am. Can you tell me the purpose for your visit?"

"I have an appointment with the school counselor. He called about my daughter, but I can't remember his name."

"There are several counselors here. Was it Mrs. Jacobs, Mr. Bell, Mr. Carson, Mr. Glascow or Mrs. Elly? Let me know so I can ring their office and let them know you're here."

I pretended to be confused. "I . . . I'm so embarrassed. I'm not really sure who I've been speaking to, but I do know it was a man. A really nice man who seemed concerned about my daughter."

"Well, go to the office and sign in. The counselors' office is to the far left inside. Tell them your daughter's name and I'm sure someone will be able to assist you further."

"Thanks so much. Have a good day, sir."

I walked in and merged to the right where the main office was. It was rather crowded and quite noisy. A loud copy machine was being used, phones were ringing off the hook and I heard loud whistling coming from the gym. It was right beside the main office. Instead of signing in as I was told, I sat next to another woman who was on her cellphone. She was venting about her daughter being suspended.

"I don't know what Carmen's damn problem is. She always caught up in some shit, and got me up here embarrassing my damn self. The principal in there talking to her now. I can't wait to get into his shit, and when I get home I'mma put my foot in her ass."

As she kept running her mouth, several students were in a group talking. Two receptionists were on the phones, and other grown folks were walking around talking to each other as well. I saw the counselors' section, but instead of going to the receptionist's desk, I waited to see if the right opportunity presented itself for me to make my move. I'd thought about the gun in my purse. I mean, what if I used it to shoot that motherfucker dead right here? I envisioned him lying on the floor with a bullet in his head. Then I heard screams. I saw so much fear in these kids' eyes and the security guard who'd let me in was strapped. Surely, he would shoot me dead. Things couldn't get that messy, today, but tomorrow could be a whole different story.

"Miss Franklin," the tall, lanky white principal said to the woman next to me. "Come this way. I'm ready to see you now."

"Girl, I gotta go. I'll tell you what happened later. Bye."

Smelling like hot fish grease, she got up and made her way up to the principal. I had to laugh at that poor man. He didn't know what he was getting himself into with her. According to her conversation, she was about to let him and her daughter have it. Waiting for that moment to arrive, I flagged down a female student who was waiting by the door with several books in her hands.

"Excuse me," I politely said. "But are you familiar with a counselor, Mr. Carson, who works here?"

"Yes I am. He's the counselor for seniors. Did you need me to get him for you?"

"I'm in no hurry. The receptionist over there said she paged him to come to the office. I need to talk to him about my daughter, Carmen Franklin. He seems like a nice man, but then again I'm not so sure."

"Mr. Carson is cool as hell. Mostly everybody likes him and we respect him around here. I don't know who your daughter is, but I'm sure he can help you and her, with whatever y'all going through."

"Are you sure, because my daughter said he was kind of sneaky. She mentioned to me before that he'd said some things to her that made her a little uncomfortable. Have you ever heard anything like that before?"

She shrugged, and for whatever reason, her mood changed. "All I know is he's cool. There were one or two students, girls, who mentioned something to that effect before, but rumors spread like wildfire around here. We don't believe—"

She looked over my shoulder and pointed her finger. "There he is. I know you've been waiting to talk to him, and that's him right there."

I felt frozen in time. My heart raced and I closed my eyes for a second, just to say a quick prayer. I asked God to give me strength and not allow me to kill this man right here. The timing wasn't right, but I wasn't sure what I'd do when my eyes landed on him. I slowly turned. Yes, there he was. Brent Carson. The man who had taken so much from me. The man who had lied to me and made me promises he refused to keep. The asshole who had raped my daughter and was now the father of my grandchild. It was him. Standing there smiling while speaking to a student. Handsome as ever, but dog-ass nigga was written all over him. His navy suit clung to his tall frame, bald head had a deep shine, white shirt was crisp, and the diamond earring I bought him was still in his ear. Maybe it wasn't the one I'd purchased, but a diamond was there. His pearly whites glistened, and the female student he spoke to appeared mesmerized. Then again, maybe it was just me. I reminded myself how much I hated him. That's what caused me to reach into my purse and touch the gun, just in case I needed it.

"Are you okay?" the female student I'd been speaking to asked. "I said that's him right there."

"I heard you. He's talking to someone right now. I don't want to interrupt him."

"Gotcha. Well, good luck. I hope everything works out with your daughter."

I thanked her, before she walked away. I wanted to make sure Brent saw me, so I moved closer to the receptionist area where he stood. I put my cellphone up to my ear, and released a slight chuckle to get his attention. From the corner of my eye, I saw him look away from the student and glance at me.

"Of course I will, honey. I'm at her school right now, but I'll be home in about an hour to cook dinner. Text me a few items you want from the grocery store."

As I spoke to no one, I turned my head to look at Brent. He was still conversing with the student, but there was no question that I had his attention. A fake smile appeared on my face; he flashed me a smile as well. After that, I walked off and kept my fake conversation going. I expected Brent to follow me, but when I turned around, he was making his way towards the principal's office. There was a bunch of loud cussing and fussing going on, and I could hear the woman from earlier going off on somebody.

"Y'all muthafuckers got me messed up! She shouldn't be suspended for no gotdamn ten days, specially not for cutting no stupid ass class. How ridiculous is that? It's a shame how y'all do these kids."

The principal didn't say anything, but Brent came to his defense. "Miss Franklin, you and your daughter need to leave the premises. Carmen will be suspended for ten days, and by then, maybe you can get her to understand why there are consequences for skipping class."

Catching everyone off guard, Miss Franklin reached out and tried to punch Brent. It was a swift punch that caused him to jerk his head back to avoid it. I wanted to laugh my ass off, but all I did was cover my mouth and pretend to be in shock by the woman's actions I totally approved. I wanted her to fuck him up!

"Go get security," the principal said to the receptionist. Everybody was looking, and crowds of people started to form around the office. Brent rushed away from the woman. He was moving so fast, that when I purposely bumped into him, he damn near knocked me on my ass. I stumbled, but he grabbed my arm to break my fake fall.

"I'm so sorry," he said, panicking. "I was trying to go get security. Are you okay?"

I straightened my suit jacket, pretending that the bump really had shaken me. "Yeah, uh, I'm fine. Just a little dizzy, but I think I'll be okay. My shoulder is a little sore."

"Why don't you stay, I mean, maybe you should go to the nurse's office. Just wait right here. I'll be back."

He rushed off to get security. In a matter of minutes, both of them came back, but I was nowhere to be found. I could see him looking around for me, as two security guards had to escort Miss Franklin out of the office. The situation was chaotic, and as many more students and teachers gathered around, I couldn't even see Brent anymore. I did, however, see the young lady I had spoken to earlier. I pulled her aside to inquire about something she had said.

"Hey, I had a chance to have a brief conversation with Mr. Carson. His attitude was terrible, and I do believe what my daughter said about him. By chance, do you know the names of the two other girls who complained about him? I'm not trying to start anything, but I just want to talk to them about their experience, if you don't mind."

At first, she seemed reluctant to say anything. But as I pushed a little more, she gave me the girls' names. "April still goes here, but the other one, Toya, she doesn't. She dropped out of school a few months ago."

"Do you know where I might be able to find her?"

"Not really. She don't really hang out a lot. Kind of weird, if you ask me. All I can say is check social media. You can find anybody you're looking for on there."

"Thanks. I appreciate the information. Stay safe and keep pushing."

"I will."

I didn't want anyone to notice me lurking around and talking with the students, so I left. I went to my car, relieved that Brent didn't suspect anything with me. There was nothing awkward in his eyes when he looked at me, and I wasn't surprised by the lustful gaze either. He was a sucker for beautiful women. Unfortunately, his charming ways could instantly lure a woman in and that's what was so scary.

School had let out. As soon as the school buses pulled away, I started to see a few teachers leave the building. More teachers followed, and ten minutes after I saw the security guard leave, I saw Brent walk out of the building. He carried several books in his hand, and a leather backpack hung from his shoulder. Another female student was with him; he appeared to be lecturing her about something. Both of them had serious looks on their faces. She kept nodding, and after he walked her to a beat-up Chevy, he made his way to his car. It was a gray, older model BMW with a sunroof. He opened it to bring in the fresh air, and then shielded his eyes with tinted shades, before driving off. I definitely wanted to know where he lived, so I followed him. Followed him for thirty minutes, as he made his way to the Central West End area, where many upscale folks in St. Louis lived. The large brick homes were like mansions. I couldn't believe Brent had upgraded his status like this. Then again, maybe he hadn't. I saw him drive to a nearby grocery store and park his car. After he did, so did I. I went inside, and right after I snatched up a basket, I shopped for food. Brent stopped at the seafood counter to get fish. He also got some bread, wine and a chocolate cake. When he made his way to the checkout counter, so did I. I was one lane over from the one he was in, but it wasn't long before he spotted me. I sparked up a conversation with the cashier, knowing Brent was watching me.

"Every time I come here, I can never find my favorite fruit bars. They had them once before, but never again. I guess they're pretty popular."

The cashier laughed. "I'm not sure which ones you're talking about, but let me know. I can check with the manager to see when we'll be getting some more in."

"It's no big deal. The other grocery store I go to carries them, so I'll continue to purchase them from there."

As I continued to converse with the cashier, I saw Brent walking slowly towards the door. I figured he was waiting on me, so I took my sweet little time. By the time I was finished, he was already out the door. He was in his car, pretending like he had just parked to go inside. Slick ass. He was so slick. As I placed my cart in the cart area, he opened the door to his car.

"What a surprise?" he said, walking up to me with his suit jacket pulled back and one hand dipped in his pocket. That's how men stood when they wanted a woman to get a glimpse of their package. He knew my eyes would shift to where his hand was. "I was just getting ready to go inside to grab a few things and here you are, again."

Lying ass nigga, I thought. A smile was on my face; I played this game right along with him. "Yes. How ironic is this? I left right after the incident at school. Did everything turn out okay? You didn't have to almost knock anyone else down, did you?"

"No, I didn't. And I'm so sorry about that, really I am. I felt so bad about it, too. I wanted to apologize to you again, but when I looked around, you were gone."

"Well, apology accepted, Mister?"

He held out his hand to shake mine. "Brent Carson."

"Okay Brent. I'm Viola Cummings. Nice to meet you, and I promise you that you didn't hurt me too bad."

Like hell. I wanted to choke from saying those words.

"Good. Cause if I had, it would've ruined my day. I was actually worried, as well as concerned about you. It's so funny that I'm standing here talking to you right now."

"Yes. What a coincidence? But, uh, thanks for the apologies. I have to get going. It's getting rather late."

"Yeah, it is. I guess you have to get home and cook your man the meal you promised him, huh?"

I cocked my head back and squinted with fake confusion. Of course he was tuned in to my fake conversation earlier. Men like him always snooped around.

"What? How did you know—"

"You were kind of loud on the phone earlier. I assumed you were speaking to your man."

"I was. My husband to be exact."

"So, you're married?"

"Happily married."

"Then, why isn't there a ring on your finger?"

"Why are you asking me personal questions?"

"Maybe because I feel bad about almost knocking you on your ass. I'd love to take you to dinner and make it up to you."

I blushed. I had this fool eating out of the palms of my hands. He didn't even know who I was. I could've shot his ass right then and there. It would be so easy to end this right now, but I didn't want to. What I wanted was to toy around with him, hurt his feelings and then see him suffer. I needed him to suffer like I did—it would make me feel so much better.

"Take me to dinner? Didn't I just tell you I was married? My husband wouldn't approve of you taking me to dinner. He'd be too jealous and I wouldn't want to hurt his feeling like that."

"What your husband don't know won't hurt."

"What about your wife?"

"What wife?"

"Aren't you married?"

"Hell, no, I'm not married. Not that I'm against marriage or anything like that, but I just haven't found the right woman yet."

In that moment, I wanted to reached out and slap the shit out of him. Same game, different day. This fool was pathetic. How could he stand there and lie like this? I couldn't believe it. Then again, yes I could. This was Brent Carson, being Brent Carson. He didn't care who he hurt. As long as he got what he wanted, everything was good. I couldn't help but wonder where Lajuanna was.

"Maybe one day you'll find the right woman," I said. "Plenty of us out there for sure."

"Or just maybe, she's standing in front of me right now. Maybe, she's not wearing a ring because she's dissatisfied with her husband. And maybe, she'll let me take her to dinner like I'd asked."

I swear I wanted to bust his bubble right here. Instead, I told him exactly what he wanted to hear.

"You've done your homework and have already figured me out. And since you're so smart, yes, I'll let you take me to dinner. Call me soon. Tell me where to meet you, and I'll do my best to be there."

"Bet," he said with a wide smile on his face. He truly thought his mission had been accomplished. I couldn't wait to play his ass like a fiddle, and then blow this thing wide open.

"See you soon," I said, as he locked my number into his phone and walked away.

"Looking forward to seeing you again, too."

I hopped in the car, feeling real good about what had just happened. Then, my face fell flat. It was only day one, and I had already screwed up. I forgot that when I left the message on his voicemail, claiming to be Francine, I had also left my number. He called that number already, and punched the same number into his phone. I hoped like hell that he wouldn't put two-and-two together and question me about the call. *Damn,* I thought. I definitely had to be more careful. This wasn't going to be as easy as I thought it would be.

CHAPTER FIVE

Several days later, I sat at Blueberry Hill in the Delmar Loop, waiting for Brent to arrive. I'd been following him around and had discovered some very interesting things. First of all, he lived alone in a loft apartment in the Central West End. His loft was on the fifth floor and it only had one bedroom. Lajuanna did not reside there with him. I had no idea where she was; it was as if she had totally disappeared. Since she was in the military, there was a possibility that she was on duty. Even if she was, Brent was being unfaithful to her. A few nights ago, I saw him go to an apartment complex near the school where he worked. It was dark outside, so I couldn't see who the woman was when she came to the door. I did, however, know that he stayed all night. His clothes were disheveled when he left, and it didn't even look like he had washed his ass. I saw him gathering himself while in the car, before entering the school to work.

Obviously, the chick in the apartment was some kind of late night side-ho. He'd only been there once, and the rest of the nights he stayed in his apartment. Other than that, I saw him flirting at the gym with several women. He even kissed the one he'd walk to her car, and I wasn't so sure if she was the one at the apartment or not. It was a lot to keep up with his messiness. I had just gotten started, and for now, following him and knowing his whereabouts seemed kind of fun.

With a fitted, off-the-shoulder peach dress on, I waited patiently for Brent to come my way. He had entered the restaurant a few minutes ago, but had stopped at a table to converse with a group of people he knew. He seemed eager to come my way. I saw him eyeing me from a far. Lust filled his eyes—I figured he thought he would get lucky tonight.

"Hey you," I said, as he walked up to the bar. "I thought you'd never get here."

"Oh, you'd better believe I was coming. As a matter of fact, I couldn't wait to get here and see you again. You look nice."

I had to admit that I really did. I was going all out this time, and I needed to do everything I could to keep his attention focused on me. My boobs sat up nice and pretty. I couldn't wait for him to get a glimpse of my ass that clearly showed through the stretch fabric of my dress. Without any panties on, I was sure he would be all over me.

"You look nice too, Brent. So well groomed, and you know us women appreciate that."

He laughed and sat right next to me. He was all up in my space, but at least his musky cologne smelled nice. His dark jeans were heavily starched and a stretch, royal blue shirt he wore melted on his biceps. Brent was never a real cocky man, but he had just enough muscles to keep women excited. Then again, his shiny bald head and neatly trimmed goatee was enough.

"I swear you look like Morris Chestnut's twin," I said. "I'm sure you hear that a lot, don't you?"

"All the time. I've been asked for my autograph plenty of times. If I'm in the mood, I'll actually sign his name."

"Noooooo," I said, laughing. Dirty bastard. Now who would do some shit like that? Only his ass. I was going to reach out to Morris Chestnut on Instagram and tell him.

"Yes," Brent added. "Anything to make the ladies feel good."

I picked up the glass of water I'd been drinking, just so I wouldn't reply to what he'd said. He didn't give a fuck about how we felt. The lies, lies, lies. This was going to be a lot harder than I'd thought. My slick mouth was bound to get me busted tonight.

"Well, we love men who know how to make us feel good and who are never afraid to tell the truth."

He laughed, before flagging down the bartender to order our drinks. "I'm having some Patron. What about you?" he asked.

"A diet coke will be fine. I don't really drink that much alcohol."

"Are you sure? And what about something to eat? They have the best burgers here."

"I know. I've been here with my husband, plenty of times. I'll have the Blueberry burger with a basket of fries. And maybe I'll have something to drink after all. I'll drink Patron, too."

"Sounds good to me."

He ordered our stuff, and for the next thirty minutes or so, we chatted about his job, his hobbies, his friends, his enemies and his favorite sports teams. He barely asked me anything about me, but that was okay. The least he knew, the better. The conversation, however, got a little sticky when he said something that left me speechless.

"You remind me of someone. I can't quite put my finger on it, but I feel like I've been here before."

Yikes, I thought. I shrugged and tossed back the Patron so fast that I almost choked.

"Who?" I questioned. "Your mom, sister, ex-girlfriend? Who exactly do I remind you of?"

"I don't know. There's something about you that is turning me the hell on. You damn sure don't remind me of my mother, or my sister for sure. Maybe an ex."

I chuckled. "I can assure you that there is only one little ol' me. Your ex will never be able to compare. You'll just have to wait and see why I'm so confident about that."

"Now, that kind of talk truly excites me. Why don't we finish up and go back to my place. I have something in mind that I need to show you."

I chuckled again. Even though I was slightly tipsy, I still had my head on straight. I couldn't get too wasted and let Brent take advantage of me. That wasn't the plan. It wasn't my plan to go to his apartment either, but less than an hour later, there I was standing in his kitchen. It was open to the living room and dining area. Everything was rather simple, yet clean. The apartment smelled masculine just like him, and with hardwood floors throughout, and glass windows surrounding the rooms, it was kind of cozy.

"You know you don't have to stand in the kitchen, right?" he said. "Why don't you come over to the couch with me and have a seat?"

I don't know why I was a little nervous, as well as scared. I mean, what if he knew who I was and just wasn't saying anything? He was good at playing games. If he suspected anything, I knew Brent would hurt me. If not that, he'd call the police and demand that I be sent back to jail.

I placed my purse on the counter and trotted over to the sofa where he was. I purposely put my ass in his face, and when I sat down, I made sure that my dress was hiked up enough to show my smooth, toned legs and thighs. I saw him bite into his lip, and when I looked between his legs, his dick print started to swell.

"If you don't mind me saying," he said in a manipulative, soft tone. "You are so damn sexy. I feel lucky to be here with you, and I have to admit that I'm super jealous of your husband. How did he get so lucky?"

With a smirk on my face, I sat back on the sofa and crossed my legs. "You don't have to be jealous of him. If anything, he might be jealous of you."

"Why's that?"

"Because you're so much cuter and sexier than he is. He's much older and you're like what? Thirty-five, forty...what?"

"One year away from forty. What about you?"

"I'm one hour away from being horny and my age really has nothing to do with that."

He laughed and nodded. Taking action after my comment, he pulled his shirt over his head and sat back on the sofa next to me. From the look in his eyes, it was time for the blunt Brent to show up. The one who was adamant about what he wanted and clear about it.

"So, what's next for us?" he asked. "You gon' let me in or do I have to stay out in the cold for a while?"

All this fake laughing and giggling made me nauseous. "Let you in? What exactly does that mean?"

"You know what it means? It means, can I hit that or is it too soon?"

"Wow, okay. Hit that, huh? I guess it depends."

"Depends on what?"

"You know what matters the most to some women. It depends on how big it is."

"Aw, it's big. Real big, so you don't have to worry about that."

I rolled my eyes. Lying ass bastard. "That's what they all say. I don't believe you."

"You don't have to take my word for it. Just let me show you. Then, you can feel it for yourself."

Proud of what he was working with, Brent stood and stepped out of his jeans. He left his briefs on, just so I could see his print that I had seen plenty of times before. While it wasn't as big as he'd made it out to be, it still was a doable size. Of course, I would never admit that. My purpose was to make him feel as insecure as he'd made me feel. Then kill him.

"I can't see anything with your briefs still on. Are you afraid to show me just how big it is?"

"Not at all. I'm just taking my time because I didn't want it to scare you. Don't get scared, alright?"

I swear I wanted to punch him in his face. This shit was childish, and how many women would admit to being afraid of dick? I was almost forty—what in the hell did I look like being afraid of dick at this age? He needed to do better. Silly ass.

"I promise I won't be scared," I said.

Brent removed his briefs and bravely stood naked before me. He was proud of his body, and of the so-called *prize* that swung between his legs. It sure as hell brought back many memories. And as I thought about this motherfucker raping my daughter, I swear I wanted to grab it and yank it from his body. I stared at it and swallowed hard.

"What are you thinking?" he asked. "You wanna touch it or feel it inside of you? Have it your way, baby, just let me know."

I uncrossed my legs and sat up straight. Since it was right in front of me, I touched it with my hand and squeezed it. Brent groaned and slowly shut his eyes. I guess he thought I was about to stroke or coat it with my saliva, but that wasn't going to happen. Instead, I lifted it, stretched it to the right, then left. I poked at his pee hole, and then brushed my fingers against his hairs. When he opened his eyes, I released his meat and sat back on the sofa, crossing my legs again.

"What?" he said with a quirky look etched on his face. "What's wrong?"

I glanced at my chipped nail polish and shrugged my shoulder. "Nothing."

"Nothing? Apparently, something is wrong. Are you concerned about your husband?"

"What makes you think I'm concerned about my husband?"

"I don't know. Maybe after we have sex, he may feel a little lost in there, if you know what I mean."

"I know what you mean, but to be honest, Brent, I'm slightly disappointed. My husband is almost fifty years old, and his penis is waaaaay more bigger than yours is. He has no problem getting it up, and I just don't like to have sex with men who have so much hair down there."

Brent laughed. "I see you got jokes, right?"

My expression was as serious as ever. "No, actually, I'm not joking. I thought you would be much bigger than that, especially since you bragged about it."

"What?" His whole demeanor changed. "I didn't brag about it. You asked and I told you it was big. I'm sorry you're disappointed. If your husband is so much bigger, then why don't you go home to him?"

I immediately stood and caused him to back away from me. He appeared shocked by my reaction and stood with his mouth open.

"I guess I will go," I said. "Sorry things didn't work out, but thanks for the dinner and drinks. Whether you know it or not, I really had a good time."

I kissed his cheek, and then stepped away from him. He was so shook that he didn't even notice when I swiped his key from the counter, hiding it in my hand. I removed my purse from the counter, too, and headed towards the door.

"Viola," he said softly. "You know it's not always about the size, don't you? I assure you that I can satisfy you in every way possible. Just let me show you what I can do."

I stood by the door, looking at his pitiful ass. It felt so awkward seeing him like this. I'd never seen him so desperate. Maybe because I'd always given him every single thing he wanted. All he had to do was snap his fingers and I was there. Whenever he wanted sex, my legs were wide open. I never put up a fuss about anything. That's why when he dumped my ass, it was a hard pill for me to swallow.

"Maybe some other time, Brent. I'm not feeling up to it anymore. Call me in a few weeks or so, okay?"

Before he could say anything, I opened the door and walked out. I couldn't even get to my car, before he'd sent me a text message.

SORRY THINGS DIDN'T WORK OUT AS PLANNED. NEXT TIME, I'LL DO BETTER.

I cut my eyes at the phone, thinking about how I was going to come back later tonight and finish this bastard off.

CHAPTER SIX

Now that I was done toying with Brent, it was time for me to make him pay for everything. Seeing him earlier and being in his presence irked my soul. How dare he think he could trick me into having sex with him. I was disgusted by his childish behavior from earlier; he really thought he was about to get the goodies. The games were over, and I hadn't escaped for nothing. Kendal hadn't been raped by him, just so he could go on living his life like he didn't have a care in the world. That's not how this worked. That's not how it was going to work, because after tonight, Brent Carson would be no more.

With a cap pulled down over my head and dark shades on, I used the key I'd stolen earlier to unlock the door to his apartment. By now, I figured he'd be in a deep sleep. What better way for me to blow his brains out when he didn't even see me coming. I smiled at the thought. My excitement was building by the minute, and as I tiptoed down the hallway, I could hear light snores coming from his bedroom. The door was wide open, and there he was, lying sideways with red silk sheets covering him. The room was dim, but I could see just enough of him through lights from the outside, cracking through the curtains. The smell of his funky cigar smoke irritated me, as did his louder snores that let me know how much he was enjoying his rest. I stepped further into the room and stood a few feet away from the bed. The gun was heavy, but I held it tight in my hand. My fear was no more. I was ready to shoot this motherfucker, and the second I lifted the gun to do it, he shifted in bed. He cleared his throat and moaned like he was dreaming. That's when I decided to let him know I was there. I jumped on top of him like a raging bull. Started pounded him with my fists, swinging on him like a madwoman. The gun was still in my hand, and as I struck him with it, time and time again, I let him know how I felt.

"You dirty son of a bitch! My fucking daughter, Brent! You raped my gotdamn daughter!"

"Noooooooooooooo," somebody said, as I curled my finger around the trigger. The red sheet blew back like a balloon and that's when I saw a light-skinned young lady with no clothes on. She was scared out of her mind. Tears ran down her face and she shook all over. With her hands in the air, and a busted lip, she begged me not to kill her.

"I . . . I'm sorry," she shouted. "I didn't know he was married! Please don't kill meeeeee. I'll go and never come back again!"

I was stunned. I quickly dropped the gun and hurried to try and comfort the young girl who almost left me speechless. God if I had killed her, I never would've forgiven myself.

"No, no, I'm not Brent's wife." I spoke in a panic, trying to hold and calm her. She pushed me away and still seemed afraid of me.

"Who are you then?" She trembled as she reached for the sheet to cover herself. "Why are you here? Were you trying to kill him?"

Of course I couldn't answer her. And without knowing where Brent was, I knew time wasn't on my side.

"It doesn't matter why I'm here. Why are you here and how old are you?"

She didn't answer me. She was afraid to answer me, and as she scooted off the bed, I reached for the gun, hurrying off the bed, too. I flicked on the lights while holding the gun beside my leg. I didn't mean to scare her, but I needed answers.

"How old are you and where is Brent?"

Her eyes shifted to the gun that I tapped against my leg. She smacked her tears away, before answering me.

"I'm nineteen. Brent left about an hour ago. All he said was he'd be back. He didn't give me a specific time."

"You're not nineteen," I said, looking at her very young features. "You're younger than that and you don't have to lie to protect him."

Yet again, she didn't respond. I needed to hurry up and get out of there. I wanted her to leave, too. This time, with an evil glare in my eyes, I pointed the gun at her and threatened her.

"Hurry up, put on your clothes and get the hell out of here. Don't you ever come back, you hear me?"

She nodded and looked at her clothes sprawled on the floor.

"If you contact him or tell him I was here," I continued. "I will hurt you and your family. Don't say anything to him or anyone else about this. Got it?"

She nodded again while snatching up her clothes from the floor. As she hurried to put them on, I kept stepping into the hallway to see if Brent was coming. So far, there was no sign of him.

"Hurry," I said as she slipped on one tennis shoe. "Did you drive here or did he pick you up?"

"I drove. My car is in the parking garage."

She barely had time to step into her other shoe, before I shoved her out of the room and ordered her to go. Once I opened the door, she sprinted towards the stairs, running like her life depended on it. At that moment, I realized what a big mistake this was. I had to slow things down and plan this out a little better. It appeared that Brent was doing way more shit than I'd thought he was. That girl had lied about her age; I was sure of it. I was also sure that I needed to find out more about what Brent was doing behind closed doors. Maybe having him arrested and thrown in jail, like I was, was the best remedy. Right as that thought crossed my mind, I'd thought about getting the young lady's name and contact information for the police. But by the time I'd rushed to the parking garage, she was gone. The proof I needed to bring down Brent Carson was gone. Now I needed to get more proof, without calling Kendal to disturb her. Surely she wouldn't want to testify against Brent. It would be too much for her—maybe even for me as well. But if there were more girls like the one I'd seen tonight, I wanted to find them. I had to find Toya and April, talk to them and do it fast.

CHAPTER SEVEN

After what had happened, I ignored Brent's phone calls and text messages. For one, I was still shaken about almost killing that young girl, and I also wanted to see if she had said anything to Brent about it. If so, maybe he would mention it to me in one of his messages. Instead, he was getting pissed at me for not responding to him. The last message he'd left was real shitty: *This is so fucked up. I don't know what I did to you, but your actions are foul. If you're feeling guilty because you're married, just say so. It makes no sense for you to ignore my calls. This is the last time you'll hear from me.*

I didn't want to take the risk of not hearing from him again, so I made a mental note to contact him later. In the meantime, I had still been watching his every single move. He had been to his side-ho's apartment twice, had taken his gym buddy to the movies, gone to dinner with another chick and never missed a day of work. I wanted to know why Lajuanna hadn't shown up, and I also wanted to find out so much more about Toya and April. I knew what men like him were capable of, but it would take me a little more time to put all of the missing pieces of the puzzle together. I had been so busy following Brent around that I hadn't had a chance to reach out to Sade's uncle. I'd gotten his direct contact information from Jeff. He'd gotten it from a client of his who claimed to know Governor Johnson well. Before I called him, I contacted Brent to tell him how sorry I was for not returning his calls. I also wanted to see if he would mention anything about the *break in.*

"I've been busy," I said. "My husband's been upset with me for being away from home so much."

"How often are you away from home? I don't mean to pry, but are you seeing someone else?"

"No, I'm not Brent. I'm just trying hard to make my marriage work. A part of me regret—"

He quickly cut me off. I sensed his little attitude. "You shouldn't regret anything. We haven't done anything for you to regret. While you seem to be concerned about your marriage, I'm not so sure about that."

"Why would you imply that?"

"For starters, you don't even wear your ring. There's a reason for that. Plus, when I search into your eyes, I see a lot of sadness there. I know it doesn't have anything to do with me, so you may have to rethink how bad you really want your marriage to work. Don't stay married, if you're unhappy. That's not good. Take it from someone who knows."

That fast, I had to call him out on the lie he'd told me. It felt good. "So, you were married before? I thought you told me you just hadn't found the right person."

"Years ago. I was married many, many years ago and things didn't work out. I was one unhappy camper. Real unhappy and we both decided it was best to move on. All I'm saying to you is don't stay if you don't want to. I'm here if you need me and I would love to see you again. When can I see you?"

I paused like it was taking me a while to think. "I . . . I'm not sure. Maybe this weekend. I'll call you Friday or Saturday."

"Hopefully, Friday. Maybe we can go check out a movie or something."

"Sure. Sounds like fun. But, uh, did you get some rest after I left the other night? You seemed a little bothered. I hope you didn't lose any sleep."

"Nah, I'm good. I'm over it and I'm looking forward to seeing you again."

"Cool, but I gotta go, okay? My husband is calling me."

I hit the end button on my phone, wondering if Brent suspected anything. I'd find out more later. In the meantime, my gut was telling me to be extremely careful.

While pacing back and forth in the living room, I held the phone to my ear, waiting for Governor Johnson to answer. I paused the second I'd heard his intimidating, masculine voice.

"I said, Governor Johnson speaking. Who's there?"

"Hello, sir. My name is Viola Cummings. I'm calling because I want to speak to you about your niece, Sade. I met her a while back. She mentioned you several times and—"

He interrupted me. "What do you know about my niece? Have you spoken to her?"

"It's been a long time since I've spoken to her, but we've always been good friends. When I heard about what she did, I felt so bad for her. From what I've heard about the situation, it sounds like self-defense to me. I'm calling because I hope you can help her out and get her out of jail. She doesn't belong there. I hope you know that, and as the governor of this state, I assume there's something you can do."

"I guess Sade must've told you a bunch of lies. She is my niece, but I don't claim her anymore. She's dangerous. I advise you to stay as far away from her as you can."

"Dangerous? I don't think we're talking about the same person. The Sade I know is very sweet. She made some bad choices, but—"

"Bad choices? That's putting it mildly. She attempted to kill her brother. Her own brother. If it had not been for her fiancé coming in the room at the right time, my nephew would be dead. She's a drug addict and she's always been very disrespectful to my sister. I would never do anything to help her. Quite frankly, young lady, you're wasting your time calling me."

"Maybe I am, and trust me when I say I don't have all of the facts. But it seems like you don't have the story straight. Her fiancé was there because he was in a sexual relationship with your nephew. Sade caught them in bed together, and did what she thought she had to do. You can't blame her for being upset. I don't know if she's done drugs, I can't say how she treated your sister, but please see what you can do to get the facts. You know a lot of people in high places. They can find out the truth. If you think she doesn't belong in jail, do whatever you can to get her out of there. She's been through a lot. Trust me, I know. That's all I ask, and I thank you for taking the time to hear me out."

Feeling like I'd done all that I could do for Sade, I stood still and waited. Waited for him to say something—anything.

"I'll look into it. Maybe it's worth looking into and thanks for calling."

I pumped my fist and felt so relieved. His words were like music to my ears. I hoped he was being truthful with me. I was so hyped that I decided to go stalk Brent.

On a Wednesday night, you'd think he would be at home doing something constructive and getting ready for a busy work day tomorrow. Not him. He was busy alright; busy sitting in his car, making out with the woman he'd been at the gym with. I didn't know what was up with this woman. The two of them had been sneaking around. Maybe she was married and didn't want her partner to know what she was up to. I watched from a distance as they sat in the car smacking lips. They laughed a few times and I could see their hands roaming. I wanted to know just how into the new me Brent was, so as he was in the midst of a sweet little kiss with the woman, I decided to call him. I saw him break away from her and look at his phone. Then, his car door opened and he got out to take my call.

"Hey Viola, what's up? I'm surprised you called me, especially since you acted like you needed some space earlier."

"Yeah, well, I have my ups and downs. It be like that sometimes, particularly when you're married."

"You don't have to tell me. I definitely know how that is."

"I'm sure you do. But, uh, where are you? I felt bad about our conversation earlier and I could really use a friend tonight. Don't be upset with me about what I'd said, and please know that my mood swings have more to do about my husband, than they do about you."

He moved a few more inches away from the car, before answering. "Baby, listen. I don't take things like that personal. I'm, uh, about to wrap up something I was doing at church tonight. The pastor called me in to help him with something. And when he calls, you know I have to put in the work."

I just shook my head at his lies. I was already his *baby*? This was crazy. Brent was a complete, hot-ass mess. "Awww, look at you. You're so sweet. I didn't know you went to church. What church do you attend?"

"The, uh, one on Dr. Martin Luther King. It's in the city. I go when I can, but I really try to help the pastor whenever he needs me. I'm about to wrap it up though. Can I meet you somewhere?"

"What if I just come to your place again? Will you be there in about an hour?"

"Yes. I'll be there. See you soon."

Brent ended the call and tucked the phone in his pocket. Whatever he said to the woman, it didn't take long for her to exit his car and speed off the parking lot. She looked upset. A frown was on her face, and it appeared that she was talking to herself. I guess she didn't realize that whenever Brent found someone new, his other women got treated like dirt. I predicted it would soon be over with between them.

Since I knew Brent was heading home, I decided to follow the woman. I wanted to know more about her. Maybe she could tell me how to find Lajuanna.

After ten minutes of driving, she drove to a subdivision near Olivette. The houses were decent, and when she parked her car in the driveway, there was another car in front of it. I saw her lower the rearview mirror and refresh her makeup. She also combed her messy hair. In my opinion, she was very unattractive. Nothing she'd done made her look better. She looked like a crackhead. Brent must've been desperate, and I now knew she'd had a man. I saw him look out the window, the second she pulled in the driveway. He even opened the door, and as she walked up to it, he said something to her. She grinned and planted a kiss on his cheek. I was stunned by all these messy ass people. Brent was in the center of it all. After she went inside, I exited my vehicle and walked up to hers. The door was unlocked, so I got inside and started rummaging through her glove compartment. Her name, along with her husband's name, was on the registration papers for the car. Karla and Paul Simmons. There was also a badge with her name on it. She worked at a furniture store, as a manager. I kept that in mind, and before I got out, I snatched up several pieces of her mail so I could go through it later.

When I arrived at Brent's place, I kept thinking about the last time I was here. That young girl was on my mind; I kept seeing her face. I kept wondering how many others there were or had been. Was Brent hiding them somewhere? I was so curious, and even though I felt like being in his presence was dangerous, I had to take risks to find out more.

I entered Brent's apartment with a pleated, knee-length skirt and multi-silk blouse on. My red pumps had my feet aching. I couldn't wait to kick off my heels and do whatever I could to make Brent reveal his true colors and feel small in the process. As expected, he was happy to see me. Glee was in his eyes. He stood like a kid in the candy store, waiting to get a piece. He eased his arms around my waist. I thought he was going to kiss me, especially since he paused for a moment to gaze into my eyes.

"I guess I don't have to tell you how stunning you look today, do I?" he said.

"Yeah, you do. It's always good to know what you're thinking and how you feel. The compliments are nice and they do wonders for my self-esteem."

"In that case, I'll keep them coming."

At that moment, he leaned in to kiss me. I quickly turned my head to the side.

"Really?" he said. Obviously, he felt rejected. "I can't have a little kiss?"

"Not right now." I removed his arms from my waist and backed away from him. "I didn't come here for that. I told you I just wanted to talk."

He was clearly irritated, but pretended not to be. "Okay, fine. Can I get you anything to drink?"

I walked around him and made my way to the living room. As soon as I sat on the sofa, I kicked my heels off, placing them beside my feet. "No, thank you. I don't need anything to drink. Just come over here, sit down and talk to me." I patted the spot next to me.

Still dressed in his Nike sweat suit, Brent sat next to me. I placed my purse on the table in front of us and proceeded with my lies.

"I've been thinking hard about divorcing my husband. We don't seem to click anymore, and even before I met you, things were rocky. You just opened my eyes, and you've been on my mind, more than I would like for you to be. I keep thinking about us. I'm so eager to spend more time with you. The problem is, I don't like this back and forth thing. I need my own space and I need to get away from my husband. He's the money maker; therefore, he controls our finances. I have some money in the bank, but not enough for me to make the kind of moves I would like to."

Brent touched my leg and squeezed it. Every time he put his hands on me, my flesh crawled. I took a deep breath as I waited for him to respond.

"It's good to know you've been thinking about me. I've been thinking about you, too. It's like I've known you for a very long time. You seem like a perfect fit in my world. I don't want to say much about this situation with your husband, and I already said if you're unhappy then you know what to do. I'm just here to help you get through this. Tell me how I can help make this easier for you."

I rubbed my forehead, as if I felt under pressure. "I . . . I kind of hate to ask you this, but is there any way I can borrow some money? I'm so embarrassed to ask you—"

"No, don't be. You shouldn't be and don't feel bad about it. Being a high school counselor, I don't make much money. But how much do you need? Maybe you can get a loan from a bank or something."

I guess he wasn't buying what I was selling. It was time to kick things up a notch. My eyes started to fill with tears. I lowered my head and swallowed hard.

"If I could get a bank loan, I would. I can't show income because I'm not working right now. I mentioned to you before that all I do is assist people with event planning. I don't make much money doing that, and just last week, my husband removed five thousand dollars from my account. That left me with fifty bucks to my name. I've been struggling so bad. I'm ashamed—"

I paused to wipe my tears. Brent got up to get me some tissue, and as I wiped my face, he pulled me into his arms. When he planted a kiss on my forehead, I eased away from him and sat up.

"The last thing I want is for you to feel sorry for me," I said. "But I needed to get this off my chest. I don't know what you can do to help me, but anything you can do, money wise, would be much appreciated."

This fool was already starting to sweat. He was cheap and too stingy to give up anything. If he did, it wouldn't come out of his pockets or bank account. I knew that for a fact.

"I'll see what I can do, okay? I don't have much in my savings, but maybe I can get a loan to help you out."

"Thank you," I said. I reached out to hug him, and as he rubbed my back, I pulled away from him again. "I need to use the bathroom, okay?"

"Go ahead. It's a little messy in there, but you should be okay."

We both laughed. I entered the bathroom and closed the door. Nobody knew how hard it was for me to be this close to Brent and not hurt him. I needed a few minutes to calm my anxieties and take deep breaths. I breathed in and out, while also shaking my hands and tense shoulders. Stress was visible on my face; I could clearly see it while looking in the mirror. I couldn't let this take a toll on me, and I kept reminding myself how important it was for me to bring him down.

Minutes later, I flushed the toilet and washed my hands. When I left the bathroom, I saw Brent standing in the kitchen with the refrigerator door opened. He was drinking some juice from a carton. I smiled at him, and then walked over to the large windows to look outside. I could see Forest Park from his loft; the nightlights and everything lit up was so beautiful. As my back was turned, Brent came up from behind and secured his arms around me. His lips touched my neck, and that's when I cocked it to the side and slipped out of his arms again. I made my way back over to the sofa and sat down.

"Why do you always do that?" Brent asked. "Every time I touch you, it's like you don't want me to. I haven't even kissed you yet, and I'm afraid to because I'll feel rejected. You act like you like me, then again, you don't. I'm not feeling this. If I'm doing something wrong, you need to tell me."

"It's not about you, Brent. It's about me feeling guilty for being here and having feelings for you. I thought I was ready for this, but I understand that this is a day-by-day process. Just give me time, okay? I need to work through this thing with my husband, separate from him, and once I'm free, I'll feel much better."

"So, in other words, you need me to be patient."

"Yes. Be patient and bear with me. Meanwhile, I want to know more about you. Come over here and tell me something about you that will totally surprise me."

He moved towards the sofa again, but when his leg bumped the table, my purse hit the floor. All of the contents inside fell out, including the gun and numerous pieces of mail I had taken from Karla's car. Her name and address was right there. Brent apologized, dropped to one knee and started picking up everything. The letters were in his hand.

"My bad," he said, shoving some of the items back into my purse. He touched the gun and looked at me while holding it. Right then, I wanted to jump over the sofa and run.

"You really shouldn't be carrying this around like this," he said. "I know some people, mainly women, feel like they need protection at all times. But keep this in your car. Your purse is not a good idea. The gun can easily go off while in there."

Boy I was nervous. I thought I was off the hook when he put the gun back in my purse, but then there were those letters. His eyes zoomed in on one of them, so I quickly reached for his face and brought it to mine. Hated to do it, but I kissed him. In a flash, he was distracted. His tongue slipped in my mouth, and he dropped the envelope as our kiss became more intense. So intense that he eased me back on the sofa and lay on top of me. His eyes were closed, mine were wide open. I hated this feeling, and just as he seemed to get real comfortable on top of me, I snapped and chomped down hard on his tongue. So hard that his eyes shot open and he jumped back like he'd touched a hot stove. He covered his mouth with his hand and looked at me with furrowed brows.

"What the fuck was that all about?" he shouted.

I played clueless. "What? Why did you jump back like that?"

"Because you bit the shit out of my tongue, that's why!"

"No I didn't. And if I did, I certainly didn't try to. I was enjoying our kiss. You really are a great kisser."

Brent was upset. He got off the sofa, still holding his mouth. I wanted to crack the fuck up. Instead, I quickly tucked Karla's mail back into my purse and went to the kitchen to check on him. Poor baby was putting some ice in a glass.

"I'm so sorry about that," I said with fake concern. "Let me see your tongue. Maybe I bit down hard, without realizing it. I was so caught up in the moment. Awkward things happen when I get too excited."

He looked at me with a twisted face. There was no smile and the roll of his eyes implied that he didn't accept my apology. The real Brent was about to show up. The fake one had disappeared and I didn't expect *him* to return anytime soon. I rubbed his back and muffled my lips so I wouldn't laugh, as he sucked on ice.

"Let me see your tongue, Brent. Is it really that bad or are you just playing with me?"

"What the fu—hell are you talking about? Does it look like I'm playing?" He snapped and walked away from me. I wasn't about to kiss his ass, so I followed him to the living room and picked up my purse.

"Obviously, you're upset with me, so I'm going home. If you still would like to go to the movies this weekend, let me know."

I made my way to the door and left. Yeah, he was mad, but he'd get over it. I had studied him for too long and was starting to know him even better. He'd open up to me and also have my money. I was one hundred percent sure of it.

CHAPTER EIGHT

Unfortunately, it took Brent longer than I'd expected for him to cool off. He never contacted me that weekend, but the following weekend he did. In the meantime, I had been doing more digging. I was able to find out more about his relationship with Karla, and I finally got Toya's address by searching through her social media pages. She was an eighteen-year-old beautiful young girl who seemed a little lost. Her social media pages were off the chain. She had provocative photos plastered everywhere, and there was no secret that she loved attention from men. After reading through her very vulgar postings, I could tell she was troubled. I had no idea about her connection to Brent, but there definitely was one. Maybe she would open up to me; then again, maybe not. It was worth a try, so I got dressed to go see what I could find out.

As for Karla, she was just a lost and confused woman like I had been. She wasn't happy in her marriage and Brent played on her vulnerabilities. She would do anything for him. Even get her husband to apply for a loan, so she could give the money to Brent. He, in return, would give the money to me. He'd told me earlier that he pulled five thousand dollars from his bank account to help me out. That was a lie. He'd gotten the money from Karla. And the sad thing was, she and her husband were already in serious debt. The letters I'd taken from her car were mostly collection letters. I felt bad about it, but I guess she had to learn her lesson just like I did.

I pulled in front of Toya's house around three in the afternoon. To my surprise, she was sitting on the porch while two kids played kickball in the yard. I knew the house belonged to her mother, but I wasn't sure if she was home. One of her neighbors was outside washing his car, while the music inside thumped loudly. He watched as I got out of my car and made my way up the driveway.

"Damn, Toya, who is that?" he shouted. "Yo friend fine as fuck!"

"Boy, mind your own damn business," she said. "You always trying to holler at somebody."

I didn't know how Toya would react to me, but I was real cordial with her. I extended my hand and told her my name. She shook my hand, immediately telling me her mother wasn't home.

"I assume she's at work, but I'm not looking for her," I said. "I came to talk to you about something. Do you have a minute?"

"Talk to me about what?" she asked then peered over my shoulder to look at the kids playing. "I'm watching my lil' brother and sister. What's this about?"

"It's about the school counselor, Mr. Carson. Do you know him?"

I definitely had her attention. She sucked her teeth and observed me. "Are you like some social worker or something?"

"No, I'm not. I'm just the mother of a young girl who had some issues with Mr. Carson. Your name came up during one of our conversations, and I wanted to speak to you about your relationship with him."

"Relationship? What makes you think I had a relationship with him?"

"I don't know. Did you?"

She sucked her teeth again and didn't respond. When she did, she yelled for her brother and sister to come inside of the house. "You can come in, too," she said to me. "I just don't want to talk about this out here."

I was pleased she was open to talking to me. When we stepped inside, she invited me to have a seat on a metal folding chair. She sat in another one, looking at her brother who stood next to her.

"Sis, can we have some cookies," he asked.

"Go ahead, but save me some boy. Don't y'all eat all of them up, and don't eat that ice cream cause it belongs to Mama."

The kids rushed off into the kitchen. Toya turned her attention to me while resting her arms on her legs.

"What's your daughter's name? Are you April's mother?"

"No, I'm not, but her name came up during a conversation with my daughter. Her name is Ke—" I paused because I didn't want her to know Kendal's name. "It's Keisha. She said Mr. Carson did some troubling things to her. While I believe her, I just want to find out if he's done something to other young girls as well."

"Well, I don't know exactly what he did to her, but all he did to me was hurt my damn feelings."

"Hurt your feelings? How?"

She seemed reluctant to speak. And when she looked down, she kept fumbling with her nails. "What I mean is, I was sort of messing around with him. My friends and me thought he was cute, and we made a bet about who could have sex with him. He was my counselor, so I started going to see him and we talked about things I was going through. After a while, one thing just led to another. We hooked up and I fell real hard for him. I started noticing that some other girls were hanging around him a bit much, too. April was one girl, but when I confronted her, she denied being with him. I knew she was lying. He got mad at me for asking her, and we got into it real bad one day."

"Did he hit you?"

"Only after I hit him. That's why I stopped going to school. I didn't want to see him anymore and I was so hurt by how he treated me. He was so nice at school. In the beginning, he did a lot of nice things for me. Treated me better than anybody I had been with, and then he like started acting real crazy. I guess it didn't help when I called his wife and told her everything. That really did it. He was completely done with me after that."

"So you spoke to his wife Lajuanna?"

"I sure did. Told her everything. She packed up her shit and left his ass." Toya laughed, as if she was real happy about it. "Anyway, after she got ghost, he threatened to kill me. I was so afraid that he would. But things kind of settled down after that."

"Did you tell anyone else about this? What about your mother?"

"I told a few of my girlfriends, but don't nobody believe me. They think I made this shit up, and Mr. Carson denied everything. I told my mother. She's upset with me for having sex with him and for dropping out of school. I promised her that I would get my GED and maybe even go to college one day. I'm just so confused. I'm working a job to help out around here. That's all I can do right now."

"Toya, you do know that what Mr. Carson did to you could be considered a crime. He should be in jail. He needs to be and I know there are more girls—"

"See, I got a problem with that because he didn't do anything to me I didn't want him to do. I was the one who pursued him. I'm not trying to get him put in jail, and trust me when I say this ain't nothing like that R. Kelly bullshit. I'm just glad my relationship with Brent is over and I can move on."

Her words were disappointing to hear. She just didn't get it and it pained me to know how Brent had twisted her young mind. Hell, he'd twisted mine and I was a grown ass woman. This girl didn't stand a chance at getting away from him for good. He'd be back. She knew it and I bet he knew it too. Her need to protect him was one of the reasons why so many men got away with this bullshit.

"I know how you feel, Toya, but how old were you when you started having sex with him? He's an adult and he had no business having sex with you."

She was starting to get upset with me and defended him to the end. "It doesn't matter how old I was. I was the one who let him do it. I can't be mad at him because I got my feelings hurt. I destroyed that man's marriage. I feel bad about it, and for you to talk about him going to jail for this ain't fair."

I sat with my mouth open. Lord knows I had no right to consider anyone stupid, foolish or down right confused. Brent was a master at this. He knew girls like Toya and women like me and Karla would do whatever he wanted.

"I'm so sorry you feel this way. This is so much more about you getting your feelings hurt, and if you ever grow to realize or understand what he really did to you, please call me. Take down my number and call me."

She rejected my offer. "I don't want your number. As a matter of fact, I think I've said too much already. If you tell anybody what I just told you, I promise you I will say you're lying."

I was starting to get a headache. My throat ached. It took everything in me not to slap the shit out of her and shake her. But shame on me for judging.

On the drive to Brent's place, I was pissed. Pissed about what Brent had done to Toya and to me. I was a grown-ass woman who allowed him to do what he'd done. I damn near ruined my whole life messing with Brent Carson, and as of today, I was still playing games with him. I hadn't called my daughter. Hadn't seen my grandbaby—hadn't even reached out to them.

This was what I considered my second chance, and there I was wasting it on this fool.

If I ever wanted to throw in the towel, today was the day I'd felt like doing it. I sat in Brent's parking garage, debating if I even wanted to face him again. Everything about him made me sick to my stomach. I wasn't sure if I could hold in everything I'd felt inside. It was just a matter of time before I exploded, and after speaking to Toya, damn, I was so upset. I reached for my purse and removed the gun from inside of it. As I looked at it, I kept asking myself if now was the time to use it. This was what I wanted, right? If it was, why was it taking me so long to just pull the trigger and be done with this? Nobody really knew who I was. I could disappear and never, ever look back on this. Brent would be dead, and what better way to make him pay for all of this, other than with his life?

Then again, I knew why I hadn't done it. I was trying to go a different route and find evidence against Brent so the police could arrest him. That was the sensible side of me talking, and I kept struggling with this. A real tug of war was going on in my mind, but whatever it took to damage Brent for good, I was willing to go there. Would the police believe me and even investigate Brent? If so, how long would that take? I wasn't sure if trusting the police to do anything was the right way to go.

With a leather skirt jumper on, I knocked on Brent's door. I straightened my suspenders, and undid two buttons on my blouse. My makeup was glistening, and with my hair slicked to my sides, I looked pretty decent. I just didn't feel good, but it was important that I looked good. Brent opened the door wearing a burgundy, cotton robe. His apartment was dimly lit with a few candles here and there. The smell of sweet oranges infused the air, and soft music was playing in the background.

"I'm glad you came." He took my hand and pulled me further inside. "I know things haven't been going well with us, but can we start over? I hope so, especially since I was able to get some money to help you out."

His eyes shifted to the table where there was a pretty pink gift bag and card beside it. I followed him into the living room, and right after I sat down, he handed the bag to me.

"I bought this for you. Hope you like it."

I opened the bag. Inside was a lace and silk, sexy black negligee with a trail of diamonds along the straps. I remembered Brent buying me something like this before; it was when I'd thought things were so good between us.

"After you open the card, why don't you go put that on and model it for me."

I just smiled and didn't respond. Instead, I opened the card to see what it said. Inside was a Visa bankcard and receipt. The receipt showed five thousand dollars, and the card was simply signed Brent.

"This is just a start," he said. "I don't mind helping you out in any way that I can. Use the money how you wish and pay me back when you can. No rush. I just want you to make progress with ending your marriage."

I was trying my best to look excited, but there was so much anger inside of me. I knew my facial expression showed it. Brent noticed it as well.

"Please tell me what's wrong? I thought this was what you wanted. You keep turning—"

I touched his chest so he'd stop talking. "I already explained to you what was wrong. While I'm so thankful to you for giving me this money, it still doesn't stop me from feeling how I do about my marriage. I told you I feel guilty."

His tone went up a notch. "Guilty for what? You don't have a damn thing to feel guilty for. We haven't kissed, you barely let me touch you, and I guess you're not going to put on the negligee I just bought you, are you?"

I slowly moved my head from side-to-side. "No, not today. But maybe—"

Brent didn't let me finish. He smacked the bag out of my hand, causing it to fly across the room. I was kind of shocked by his childishness, and I had to admit that I was more than afraid of being here right now.

"Stop playing this fucking game with me, Viola. Either you're in or out! You're acting like you some sixteen or seventeen year old chick who doesn't know how to get her shit together."

He would know all about that, wouldn't he? Those words were on the tip of my tongue, but I didn't say it. All I'd thought about was how quickly I was going to get the gun out of my purse, if or when shit got more out of hand. For now, I tried to calm him.

"I didn't mean to upset you, Brent, but why are you so worked up? You act like I'm not entitled to take things slow with you. Whether you believe it or not, I do whatever I want."

"Yeah, and so can I."

Catching me off guard, that motherfucker backslapped me so hard that he knocked my ass on the floor. I was stunned. The whole left side of my face was on fire. I kept blinking while looking at him through a blurred vision. He jumped on top of me and was heavy as fuck. I flopped around and tried to push him off of me, but when he held my hands above my head, I could barely move. I screamed loud so somebody . . . anybody would hear me. That's when he raised his hand high and slapped the shit out of me again. This time, I felt a slow drip of blood running from my nose. Brent Carson had finally showed up. And not in the way I had exactly expected.

"Shut the fuck up," he said through gritted teeth. His devilish eyes stared into mine, as our chests heaved in and out. I seriously feared that he was going to kill me. If I could someway or somehow get to the gun in my purse, I'd be able to do exactly what I had set out to do from the beginning. Lord knows I was so mad at myself for not acting sooner. Mad that I'd decided to play this little game with him; it had backfired.

"Stop fucking whimpering and listen to me," he roared. "I don't know who the hell you think you are, but you ain't gon' play this gotdamn game with me. What you are going to do is fucking cooperate. If you don't, I'mma slice your fucking throat and dump yo ass in an alley. Let me know right now if you understand, clearly, how this shit about to go down."

Barely able to breathe with his weight on top of me, I slowly nodded my head.

"Good girl," Brent said. He freed one of his hands, and started to rub my leg. His touch made my whole body quiver, and as I squirmed around underneath him, he slammed his fist on the floor next to my face.

"Be still! I told you you'll enjoy this, didn't I? I promised you that I would make you feel good. You didn't believe me, but always remember that I'm a man of my word."

The man of his word pulled my skirt over my hips and tore my panties off. As he reached for the weapon between his legs, I was able to scramble a few inches away from him. While still on my back, I kicked my feet to keep him away from me. Tears seeped from my eyes, and I grunted loudly, ignoring his threats to hurt me if I didn't keep quiet.

"You fucking no-good bastard," I shouted.

That was all I could say and couldn't say no more. Not after his fist landed on my face and damn near knocked me clean out. My head jerked, and I felt like a damn ragdoll as he ripped my blouse to fondle my breasts, then turned me on my stomach and exposed my bare ass. He squeezed my cheeks and plunged his dick inside of me so fast that I could barely catch my breath. While thrusting hard inside of me, he held my head down so I couldn't move. The pressure was unbelievable. I laid there devastated, and after a while, I couldn't even cry anymore.

"How does it feel?" he said, then laughed. "Good, doesn't it? I told you I was good, and guess what, baby? This wet ass pussy feels pretty good, too."

I closed my eyes and licked the dripping blood away from my lips. I kept thinking about the gun in my purse, because as soon as all of this was over, I was going to use it to blow his damn brains out. I couldn't help but wonder if this was what he'd done to Kendal. How many other girls and women had he done this to? He was a pro at this, and as soon as he was done, he stood over me and sprayed his semen all over my back.

"Damn, baby, look what you made me do," he said, tightening his robe. "Now get up and go clean yourself up because you're bleeding all over the place. If you would like round two, put on the negligee I just bought you and meet me in my bedroom."

He stepped over me and casually made his way to the kitchen. I rolled on my back, and feeling sticky all over, I kept taking staggering breaths. I could see my purse on the sofa, but as I rushed off the floor to get it, Brent called my name.

"You are so fucking stupid," he said with the gun in his hand. "Did you think I didn't know you had this? I told you about carrying it around, didn't I?"

Damn. Did he know who I really was? Is that why this was happening? I waited for him to spill the beans and finally tell me I was about to die.

"If you want to use this gun," he said. "Why don't you use it on that sorry ass husband of yours? I hope you find a way to reconcile with that motherfucker, because guess what, Viola? We're done. I don't need you anymore. I got what I wanted, and quite frankly, it wasn't really all that."

He laid the gun on the counter and came back over to where I was. After tucking the greeting card and Visa card in my purse, he threw it at me. "You can keep that shit. Now get up, go clean yourself up and get the fuck out of here."

I guess I wasn't moving fast enough for him, because he yanked me up from the floor and dragged me into the bathroom. I felt so weak as he held me up from behind while wiping my battered face with a wet rag.

"Daaaaamn, I fucked you up, didn't I?" he said, jokingly. "I didn't mean to mess up your pretty face like this, but you really hurt my feelings."

He swung me around to face him and rubbed my face like he really cared. I stared at him in a daze. That prompted him to cover my lips with his, pecking them three . . . five times.

"Don't be upset, okay? I just did what I had to do. If you're mad at anyone, you should be mad at yourself for teasing me. Had you not teased me, we wouldn't even be here."

He used the rag to wipe between my legs. Once he was finished, he tossed the soiled rag in the sink and started to straighten my clothes. I stood like a zombie, but when he pecked my lips again, I gathered saliva in my mouth and shot a gob of spit in the middle of his face. I expected a swift response. That's what I got. He lit up my midsection with a hard punch that forced me back into the wall. He grabbed my throat, and as he lifted me from the floor, my feet dangled.

"Bitch, I'm done with you! I never want to see you again, and if you come on my job or reach out to me in any way, you won't live to see another day."

I coughed and gagged as he shoved me towards the door. He opened it and tossed me outside like I wasn't shit. Seconds later, he threw my purse at me, and as I made my way toward the elevator, I was a complete mess. All I could think was, how was I the one in jail, instead of him? Somebody needed to explain that to me. Maybe Officer Eric Wayne could.

CHAPTER NINE

There I was, at the police station, trying to see if they'd go arrest Brent. My gut told me this wasn't the right move, but after all the crazy shit I'd done in the past, a part of me was hoping to redeem myself. After what Brent had just done to me, I didn't think that was possible. This was my last attempt at trying to do the right thing. If it didn't work, God would just have to forgive me for taking matters into my own hands.

Per my request, I sat in a private room, waiting for Officer Eric Wayne to enter. I didn't bother to straighten myself up, and as a matter of fact, my black eye was even blacker than it was earlier. My ripped blouse exposed my bra and parts of my breasts. My skirt had stains all over it, hands were scratched up and dried blood was on my legs and arms. According to the man at the front desk, an ambulance was on the way. I told him I didn't need it. All I wanted to do was speak to Officer Wayne who was definitely on duty.

Five minutes after I had entered the room, the big man who was there to protect and serve, Officer Eric Wayne, came inside with his police uniform on. A cap was on his head; his waves flowed underneath it. He stood by the door, shocked, and with thick, furrowed brows, he couldn't stop looking at me. A notepad was in his hand, a pen was locked behind his ear.

"Officer Mason at the front desk said you asked for me. What's your name and tell me what happened to you?"

I licked my swollen lips, thinking about how this man had played me. How he tried to intimidate me and screamed at me that day in the interrogation room, when he asked if Brent Carson was worth it! I looked at him with so much hurt and pain in my eyes. My voice was soft and very measured.

"My name is Viola Cummings. I was just raped and beaten by a man who was supposed to be my boyfriend. A friend of mine told me to come here and ask for you."

Eric swaggered over to the table, displaying his bowlegged stance and good looks. He took a seat in the chair across from me. As expected, he thoroughly examined me and removed the pen from behind his ear. He cleared his throat, before questioning me.

"Raped you? What's the name of your friend who sent you here?"

"It doesn't matter." My eye twitched as I glared at him with so much anger in me. "What matters is what he did to me. He raped and beat me. I want him arrested. A monster like him should be behind bars. Wouldn't you agree?"

Eric tapped the pen against the notepad. He never took his eyes off me. He pretended to be calm, but I sensed that he really wasn't.

"From what I can see, you've been hurt real bad. And whoever did this to you, that person should be arrested. Do you want to tell me what happened?"

I sat there, sounding like a robot. "I don't need to go into details. All you have to do is look at me. Look at my face. Look at my chest. If you want, I can take off my skirt and show you what he did to my insides too."

"You don't have to do that, okay? I just need to know what happened. I need a name so I can go talk to this person and find out why he or she did this to you. You're not giving me much to go on. All I'm getting from you are a bunch of devious stares."

"I have nothing else to give you, other than a name. His name, but first I want to tell you how dangerous he is. He hurt me. Hurt me before and recently hurt me again. He raped my daughter and he's been raping young girls at the school he works for. You need to arrest him. Do it now, before it's too late."

"Do you have any proof that this man has—"

My voice remained calm. "I'm all the proof you need. Again, look at me. Do you think I've done this to myself?"

"I didn't say that. I really want to help you, but something is very strange about this whole conversation." He stopped tapping the pen and wrote something on the paper. "Tell me his name and address. I'll send an officer over there to question him tonight."

"His name is Brent Carson. B. R.E.N. T. C. A. R. S. O. N."

Eric's head snapped up. He looked like he'd stopped breathing. I watched his eyes grow wide and a little sweat was starting to build on his forehead. He blinked, numerous times. Shifted in his seat, and then wrote my name, Viola, on the paper.

"Did you say Brent Carson?"

"I sure did. Would you like for me to spell it out for you again, or did I make myself clear?"

Appearing nervous, he wiped down his face. Seconds later, he scooted his chair back and stood. He looked at me with a fake-ass smile on his face.

"Wait right here, okay? I'll be back in a few minutes."

"Take your time. I'm not going anywhere."

Like hell I wasn't. As soon as he left the room, I rushed up, cracked the door and made sure the coast was clear. Eric was nowhere in sight, but two other officers, along with another lady, stood by a desk talking. I opened the door and didn't even look their way. As I neared the exit, that's when I saw Eric exit a door with another officer by his side. He stared at me from a short distance and I looked at him.

"Abby?" he quizzed with his head cocked to the side. "Abigail Wilson?"

I turned my back, and the second I opened the door, I kicked off my shoes and took off running. I wasn't sure if he was following me or not, but once I was able to merge off to the right and hide behind a tall building, I realized that he hadn't come for me. I stood for a moment, chest heaving in and out while trying to catch my breath. My car was on the other side of the street, and after I waited for fifteen or twenty long minutes, I hurried to make my way to it. Instead of going to my apartment, I drove to Jeff's place. He pulled the door open with a smile on his face. One more glimpse, his smile vanished.

"Damn, Sweat Pea, who done beat yo ass like that? Get in here and let me show you some love."

Jeff threw his arms around me. I wasn't sure if he was being sincere, but his arms sure did feel good. I was too broken right now to talk. All I thought about was a bath and how I was going to get my mind right after this. Jeff held me up and carried me over to the couch. He felt bad for me. I wasn't able to share everything, but had shared enough. For the first time, he sat quiet and didn't say much. I didn't ask why, because I knew he didn't understand what this felt like. With my eyes closed, I sat there, in his arms, in deep thought. Flashbacks of Brent penetrating me were right there. I saw his fists landing on my face. His voice was loud as hell. He was a madman. God it hurt. It hurt that I had fallen so hard for a man like him. All of it hurt and it took me a few more hours to even talk about it and prepare to clean myself up.

"Sweet Pea," Jeff said, trying to get my attention. "Let me help you, doll. You need to clean yourself up and go lay down."

"I know, Jeff. I know what I need to do."

I wanted to cry, but didn't. What good would crying do me? I was numb all over, and after my conversation with Eric, I felt like he'd failed me too.

"Thank you," I softly whispered to Jeff.

"What are you thanking me for? Sit up and tell me everything that happened to you."

I couldn't sit up, but I spoke up. "As I said, Brent did this to me."

"I know what you said and I heard you loud and clear. From my recollection, Brent may be a whole lot of things, but a woman beater he is not. Stop lying, Sweet Pea. I know how much you hate him, and I hope you not out here playing these silly ass games again."

His comment made me sit up. Had I messed up my reputation that bad, where nobody believed me? I hated to attack him with my words, but I did.

"Jeff, screw you. There's a side to Brent that a lot of people don't know about. I wanted to bring out that side of him, and even though I knew something horrible was there, I never expected this."

I went on to tell Jeff about how everything unfolded, and about Toya, April and Karla. He wasn't shocked about that, but a part of him still couldn't believe Brent had done this to me.

"Like I said, a ho will always be a ho. Age don't matter to Brent and I've seen him with lots of women before."

"Young girls, Jeff. Some of them are really young and nobody seems to care what he's out there doing."

"It's not that people don't care, Sweet Pea, but that kind of shit been going on for a long time. Everybody fucking everybody, and not too many people are worried about what age people are, before they have sex with them. I'm not saying it's right, but that's just the way it is."

Jeff's response reminded me just how many people didn't care. I thought about my conversation with Toya. I wanted to tell Jeff about her, again, but it had been a long day. I was so exhausted.

"I can't accept that this is the way it is," I said. "Wrong is wrong. But instead of arguing about it tonight, can I please go take a shower and relax in one of your bedrooms for the night? After what happened, I'm worried. Eric knows who I am, and it's probably just a matter of time before the police step up their efforts to find me."

"I feel so bad for you, Sweet Pea. And anything else I can do to help, just let me know. With that being said, you know I always have time for jokes, no matter how serious things are. You mentioned that Brent gave you some money. I recall you saying that he would be the one to pay me back, not you. Do you have me covered?"

I reached for my purse and removed the Visa gift card from it. "Forgive me for not laughing, but I'm glad you remembered. I try to be a woman of my word. You'd better hurry to transfer the money to your account. I don't know if he will cancel the card or not, but I was surprised when he put it in my purse."

Jeff snatched the card from my hand and tucked it in his bra. "Go wash up and I'll go see if I can make a few transactions. Thanks, again, Sweet Pea. It's good to know that like the post office, you can and will deliver."

Jeff's Jacuzzi tub with waterfall faucets was everything. It was just what I needed. Once he was done transferring money from the card, he came into the bathroom to help wash me up. The soaps and fragrances he used were to die for. I felt like I was in heaven as he massaged my body with his hands and worked it with a sponge. He patted my face with ice and apologized for not believing me.

"Forgive me for saying what I said earlier. It was so stupid and I don't know why it's so hard to believe women when they go through shit like this. You're so right. Wrong is wrong. It makes me sick to my stomach to see your face like this and know that he raped you. How can any man call himself a man and do something like this?"

With my head tilted back on the contoured pillow, I agreed. "I don't know. Brent didn't hold back. It came easy for him and there is no doubt in my mind that, in addition to me and Kendal, he's done other women like that too. It just makes me think about what he did to Kendal. She didn't provide details, but I know she put up a fight when he raped her. I was too blind to see what had been going on. Brent played me and she kept quiet. She must've been afraid of him. And the sad thing is she didn't even feel safe coming to me and telling me what he'd done. That's a hard pill to swallow. I'm so ashamed of myself, Jeff. So ashamed and I can't even face her."

"Is that why you haven't reached out to her?"

"That's part of it. Then there's a part of me that feels like she's so much better off without me. She seemed to be on the right path and having to deal with all of this mess again would be so unfair to her."

"I hope you're right. I know you miss her, but I do understand what you're saying too. As for Brent, I know you've been struggling with how to handle him, but tell me this. What do you do now, Sweet Pea, especially since he has your gun?"

"Just so you know, I don't need a gun to cause damage. And whether you approve or not, I can't let this go, Jeff. I just can't let this go."

Jeff put his hands together and said the only thing he could. "I'm praying for you."

.

CHAPTER TEN

It was a good thing that I still had a key to Brent's apartment. When I entered, I heard jazz music coming through the speakers. Some of the milk and cereal he'd eaten for breakfast was left in a bowl on the table. The TV in the living room was on and there were several Sports Illustrated magazines sprawled on the table. His comforter and pillow were on the sofa, so I assumed he had chilled there last night, instead of in his bedroom. Already knowing that he was at work, I stalked down the hallway with a wooden bat beside me. Still feeling numb, I turned on the lights in his bathroom, looking exactly where I'd stood last night. What he'd done was still fresh in my mind, and I was so frustrated that I swung the bat forward, slamming it into the huge glass mirror above the sink. The mirror broke into a thousand pieces and sharp shards of glass were all over his bathroom. I was sure he'd have a fun time cleaning it up, and the thought of him doing it made me smile.

I exited the bathroom and went into his bedroom. Before I did any damage there, I laid the bat on his bed and started rummaging through his dresser drawers. I had hoped to find the gun he'd taken from me, but nothing really jumped out at me in his drawers. When I started searching through his closet, that's when I saw a duffel bag with numerous photos, letters and cards inside of it. The cards and letters were given to him by multiple women. I scanned through words in the letters and cards; all of it made me sick. Some stressed how much they loved him, while others were so grateful for his friendship. I'd even seen one of the cards I'd given to him. My loving words disgusted me so much that I ripped the card and tossed it aside. As I started looking through the photos, they were sickening as well. Many of the photos were sent to Brent, but it also seemed that he, or someone else, had taken some of the photos, too. I couldn't tell because he was in several of the photos. One in particular, he was lying there naked with a cigar dangling from his mouth, with two naked women by his side. The ones that troubled me the most were the young girls, like Toya, who just didn't seem to know better. She was in numerous photos, as was several other young girls who revealed their bodies in ways I could never see myself doing. I feared that I would come across a photo of Kendal. There were lots of photos to go through, and once I was finished, I removed eight of them and tucked them inside of my jacket. If Eric saw these, maybe it would prompt him to believe me and take action.

I put the bag back where it belonged and started searching for what else I could find. A smiled crept on my face when I saw a gray piece of luggage that had money inside of it. I didn't count how much it was, but there was a stack of hundred and fifty dollars bills. I tucked that away in my jacket, too, knowing that Jeff would appreciate it. Just as I put the luggage back, I heard a door squeak open and shut. The music I'd been listening to came to a halt. I looked at my watch; it was a little after noon. Brent was early, but in no way did it change my plans to do what I'd set out to do. Slightly nervous, though, I tiptoed out of the closet and hurried over to the bed to grab the bat. I finally heard his voice. He was still in the living room area speaking to someone over the phone.

"Yeah, I'm thankful for the half day of work. I need to get some rest. I haven't been resting well lately, and I'm not exactly sure why."

While holding my breath, I stood by his bedroom door waiting for him to enter. The bat was high up in my hand, and I kept twirling it around, trying to build up as much power as I could. I heard Brent's voice getting closer and closer. He was laughing his ass off about something, and as soon as he entered his room, I swung the bat, chopping him right in his midsection with it. He was so caught off guard that the phone dropped from his hand and he tumbled to the floor on one knee. I didn't even give him a chance to see who I was, before I swung the bat against the back of his thick neck, while beating down on his shoulders so he would fall. He crashed to the floor, flat on his face, moaning and groaning.

"Aaaaaahhhhh, shit. Fucccck, wha . . . what do you want?"

I swiftly answered by lifting the bat over my head and gripping it tight with both hands. With my legs straddled, I stood over him and crashed the bat, numerous times, against his back. His whole body jerked, and underneath his shirt, I could see his muscles tighten as he attempted to stiffen his back and minimize his pain from the blows. With his head now turned to the side, his drool oozed on the floor. The sight was beautiful. So beautiful that as I remained standing over the bastard, I ordered him to turn over.

"You heard me. Roll your ass over!"

"Who . . . who are you and what do you want?" he groaned.

The motherfucker was in a daze. Didn't even know who I was, because he had done so much dirt and didn't know who was coming for him. I wanted him to see me. To see my face and look deep into the eyes of not only a woman who he'd done wrong, but a woman he'd just raped last night.

"I said, turn over!"

In pain, Brent squeezed his eyes, held his side and rolled on his back. As he looked at me with wide eyes, I smashed the tip of the bat against his jaw and threatened him.

"If you try anything stupid, I'm going to swing this bat against your fucking face and crack it. Got it?"

He slowly nodded and I pushed the bat harder against his jaw, causing his mouth to twist more.

"Speak up, bitch! I can't hear you."

"Yes, Viola," he mumbled. "I got it."

"Good. And because you fucked with the wrong woman, I got you, too."

While he was on his back, I sent the bat flying again. This time, I raised it high and slammed it right on top of his dick. He tried to squeeze his legs together to block the blow, but I got his ass good. I laughed my ass off as he screamed like a bitch, rolled over and balled himself in a knot. His hands cuffed his wounded package and his breaths were staggered.

"Shiiiiiiiiiiiiiiiiiiiittt, gotdaaaaam-it, Viola, fuucccccck you!"

"Fuck me?" I said, pointing to my chest. "No, Brent. Fuck you!"

I kicked his leg, making him fall flat on the floor again. He was still trying to recover from the blow to his dick, and as tears seeped from the corners of his eyes, I wasn't done with him yet.

"Get on your hands and knees and crawl your ass out of here."

He gazed at me with narrow, puppy-dog eyes, trying to gain some sympathy. More spit foam oozed from his mouth and he kept shaking his head.

"I . . . I'm sorry, alright?" he muttered. "I will never do that agaaaain."

"Sorry? Nigga please. Like I said, get on your hands and knees and crawl your lame ass to the living room."

He opened his mouth, but before one word came out, I struck his leg, again, with the bat.

"Now Brent," I hollered. "Do it now!"

He struggled to get on his hands and knees, but managed to do it. As he slowly trotted down the hallway, I lifted my foot, kicking him in his ass. He fell flat on his stomach and coughed.

"Stop this, Viola," he mumbled. "If you gon' kill me, just do it and get it over with."

"Oh, so you brave now, huh? You're ready to accept your punishment and be done with this, right? Okay, then let's be done with it then. As soon as you get to the living room, and you lay in the same spot as I did last night, I'll be done. So move!"

I kicked his ass again; he grunted and crawled like an anxious dog, hurrying to get a bone.

"Now what?" he said, falling flat again. He sucked in deep breaths and grabbed his side like he was in so much pain.

"Now, you get a chance to feel every single thing that I felt last night."

With his slacks still on, I rammed the tip of the bat up his ass, as far as it would go. He hollered a little, but it wasn't enough to excite me. Since I wasn't strong enough to strip him of his clothes, like he'd done me, I tried to injure his manhood again. This time, however, when I swung the bat, he raised his arm to block me. The bat hit his arm and broke in two. Part of it flew across the room and hit the TV. Without my weapon, I knew I had to get out of there. I sprinted to the door and rushed down the stairs. Brent was too damaged to come after me, and by the time I'd made it to my car, I was happier than I'd been in a long time. The looks on his face were priceless. He was hurt and I loved it. I just didn't know what all this meant going forward.

CHAPTER ELEVEN
BRENT CARSON

For a week and a half, I stayed home from work, trying to heal myself. This was embarrassing enough for me to deal with and I didn't want anybody to know what had happened. My body ached all over, but thankfully, I didn't have any broken bones. I was upset with myself for not doing my homework on that bitch Viola. She had appeared out of nowhere. I didn't know much about her, and it was my fault for chasing a piece of ass that belonged to a crazy woman. What she'd done had shocked me. Her retaliation was brutal. I just couldn't get over it, and something about the whole situation had me on edge. Normally, I wouldn't be on edge like this. But Viola had rummaged through my shit, taken some photos and also stolen my money. The six-thousand-plus dollars I'd saved was gone. I was livid, and if I ever, in my life, saw that bitch again, I was going to kill her.

When I returned to work, I couldn't even stay focused. Today was Become an Entrepreneur Day at school, and I was one of the judges who decided which students had the most creative idea. Every time the students went on stage to provide details about their business plans, I drifted off. Thoughts of Viola swarmed in my head. The more I'd thought about what I'd done to her, she deserved what she got. I didn't feel bad about it, because she shouldn't have insulted me about my penis. She had gone too far; therefore, she shouldn't have been upset by how things had turned out.

It wasn't even like I was a bad guy or anything. I was good to women, as long as they were good to me. Viola messed up when she started messing around with my insecurities, purposely biting my tongue and toying with my emotions. She was up one minute, down the next. I didn't have time for that shit. I had to do what I did because she owed me for wasted time.

"That was awesome, Sabrina," the principal said. "Since you're the last student, we're going to discuss everything and decide who are first, second, and third place winners."

"Thank you," Sabrina replied.

She walked off stage wearing a short-ass dress that revealed her long, pretty legs. Young girls these days were something else. They were *different*, and I had so many of them coming to me and vying for my attention. It was a shame. Then again, maybe not because all of the attention also made me feel good. I wasn't trying to go there with any of them, but unfortunately, April and I made a connection, as did me and Toya. It wasn't supposed to happen that way, but it did. I was somewhat glad to be done with her. She was the one who had fucked up everything for me. When it came to involving Lajuanna, I didn't play around with that shit. Considering all that had happened with my crazy ex Abby, Lajuanna and me had been doing well. That was until Toya called and spilled the beans about us. It wasn't even that serious between us, but for some reason, Toya believed I was going to leave my wife and be with her. She didn't have anything to offer me, but a piece of wet ass. That was it, and every time I reminded her of that, she acted like a spoiled brat and got upset. Her childishness and jealousy prompted her to call Lajuanna and the rest was history. She left my ass. Said she'd had enough of my bullshit and took off. I had hurt her enough, so being the real man that I was, and still am, I let her go and didn't even fight the divorce. I did, however, cut all ties with Toya. It was my way of punishing her for what she'd done. Every now and then, I still hooked up with April, but she was starting to get a little controlling. I didn't know what was up with these young chicks thinking they could control me. How foolish was that? No, how crazy was that—the mind was a terrible thing to waste.

Due to April's fucked up mindset, I hadn't done anything with her in about two months. Just last night, though, she sent me a text, ranting about my much needed decision to distance myself. I was getting sick of her, and after what had happened with Viola, I needed a break from everyone. Another reason why I wanted to distance myself was because a big part of me didn't like obsessive females. Been there, done that. Anyone who possessed obsessive behavior was dangerous, and I knew all too well that somebody could get hurt.

Just as I was about to give my input on who I'd thought the winners were, I looked up and saw Officer E. Wayne enter the auditorium. After the situation with Abby blew over, he and I became good friends. We talked every now and then, and we also played on the same baseball team. I figured he was there to talk about baseball, but when he asked if we could talk in private, I knew it was more serious.

"Follow me to my office, E," I said, walking beside him. "By the way, how's everything been going at the station?"

"Not too bad, but my department still has a lot of work to do. We've been short on staff, and ain't too many people trying to be police officers these days. It's a little rough out there. Nonetheless, I do love my job."

"That's all that matters." I unlocked the door to my office. We went inside, and after I turned on the lights, I slowly took a seat in the chair behind my desk. My body was still aching and rather stiff too. The pain pills I'd taken were starting to wear off, so I reminded myself to take a few more, right after Eric left. He sat on the other side of my desk, examining me.

"Man, are you okay?" he asked. "You don't look well."

"Nah, I'm good. What brings you by today? The game ain't for another two weeks. I know you ain't here to beg for a little more practice."

Eric leaned back in the chair and placed his hands behind his head. "Nah, nothing like that. Something interesting happened a few weeks ago. I've been meaning to swing by here and talk to you about it, but things been kind of busy."

"Busy as hell up here, too. But what's up?"

"Do you happen to know a woman by the name of Viola Cummings?"

At that moment, I tried to play it cool. Obviously, Viola had gone to the police to tell them what I'd done. I wondered if she'd told them what she'd done.

"Yea . . . yeah, I know her. I met her several weeks ago, but for whatever reason, things didn't work out. As a matter of fact, she told me she was married and didn't want to continue our relationship. I didn't think much of it, because shit happens like that sometimes."

"Interesting," Eric said. "So, she told you she was married?"

"Yep. That's what she said."

"Did you ever meet her husband or see her with him?"

"Nope."

"Do you know where she lives or where she works?"

"Not really. All she said was she did some kind of event planning stuff and made money on the side. Our relationship wasn't that serious. I was just starting to get to know her."

"So, you never put your hands on her, huh?"

I cocked my head back and twisted my face. I had to be real careful with my words. Hoped I wasn't talking too much.

"What? Put my hands on her. Why would I do that? Nah, man. I don't hit women. The last time I saw her, she asked me for some money. She seemed to be going through something, and I wanted to help. This might sound foolish, but I let her borrow some money. A lot of money, and after she left that day, I haven't heard from her since."

"So, she took your money and ran?"

"Unfortunately, E, looking back on it, I think so. I reached out to her a few times, but she hasn't returned my calls yet. I decided to give her some space. Even though I felt played, I tried to convince myself that the reason she hadn't called was because she decided to work things out with her husband."

Eric sat with a peculiar look on his face. He stroked the hair on his chin and then sat up straight in the chair.

"Do you mind showing me where you withdrew money from your account and gave it to her? If that's what you did, you should have a record of it, right?"

It concerned me a little that he didn't believe me and was asking for receipts. But like always, I had covered my tracks.

"Listen, I'm not sure what all of this is about, but if you need to see my bank statement, cool. Even though I'm a little embarrassed by the money I gave her, I can also show you the receipt for the credit card I gave her to use."

"That would be very helpful."

I was sure it would be. And of course I expected Viola to go to the police and tell them what I'd done. But there was always a way to *clear* things up. I typed in my banking information on my computer and turned the monitor around so Eric could see it.

"Here's where I went to the bank and transferred five grand to a Visa bank card. The lady at the bank noted it as a payment for Viola Cummings. Right after I did that, I went to Victoria's Secret and purchased a negligee for her. You can see the purchase I made right there." I pointed to the Victoria's Secret purchase on my bank statement. "I was just trying to be nice, because the two of us were really starting to click. That's what I thought, until she didn't return my phone calls. Please, please, please don't tell any of the fellas about this. I already feel foolish, and I don't want nobody joking about how I got played."

"I wouldn't say a word to anyone, but I might have some real bad news to deliver to you, bro."

This time, I sat up straight. I wasn't sure what Eric was going to say. Was he about to arrest me? Yes, we were friends, good friends, but he was serious about his job. When it came to that, he didn't mess around. I was definitely tuned in to what his bad news was all about.

"Viola Cummings came to the police station and asked for me. Her face was all fucked up, eye was black, clothes were nearly ripped to shreds, and she told me you had raped and beaten her."

"What?!" I shouted and jumped from my seat. My whole face was scrunched, and pretending to be in disbelief, I shook my head from side-to-side. "I can't believe she told you that bullshit! What in the hell is going on? Have you spoken to her husband?"

"No, calm down, alright?"

I fell back in my chair and held my forehead like it hurt. "E, it's hard to stay calm, especially after hearing something like this. I can't believe she would lie on me like that. I thought Viola was cool, but damn, this is so messed up."

"It is, and unfortunately, it gets worse. All of this may start to make sense when I tell you something. About two months ago, Abigail Wilson pulled a little trick in prison and disappeared. You do remember Abby, right?"

I was starting to get confused. A knot tightened in my stomach and a tingling feeling was moving up my legs.

"Of course I remember Abby's crazy ass. How can I forget about her?"

Just saying her name made me quiver. I had just been thinking about her, too.

"Well, she escaped. In an effort not to make the warden or the officers who were on duty that day look bad, things were kind of kept on the low-low. I got wind of the news a few days after she escaped. My department was asked to stay on the lookout for her, but I figured she got out and ran to Mexico or something."

I sat there stunned. My mouth was wide open; I almost didn't know what to say.

"How in the hell was she able to escape from prison? She wasn't that damn bright, and is it that easy for somebody to just walk up out of there?"

"No, but we believe she had some help on the inside. We don't know by who yet, but we'll find out soon enough. In the meantime, I think she's coming for you, if she already hasn't."

"What in the hell is that supposed to mean? I mean, what exactly are you trying to say?"

Eric paused and looked me straight in the eyes. "It means that I have every reason to believe that Viola Cummings is actually Abigail Wilson."

I damn near fell out of my chair. Flashbacks of Viola . . . Abby beating the shit out of me was in my mind. The way she taunted me . . . kicked me in my ass, I should've known something. No way would I tell Eric what had happened. I sat up real straight; my mind was going a mile a minute. I quickly thought about the timing, thought about how we'd met, thought about the gun in her purse, and even thought about how she never wanted me to touch or kiss her. I also thought about when I had my dick in her. Her ass looked so familiar. Even the feel of her pussy—I should have known. Her voice—damn, and the money! Things were quickly starting to come together.

"Damn, E, are you serious? I mean, now that you mention it, it all makes sense."

I felt like I was in a twilight zone. This couldn't be happening right now. *Abby?*

"It does make sense. She's up to her old tricks again. Plotting, scheming and lying. I don't know who beat her up, but they did a pretty good job. She told me you did it, and she also told me you raped her daughter and had been raping other girls, too."

I slammed my hand on the desk, pissed. "Man, get the fuck outta here. Are you serious? I can't believe this is happening all over again. I thought I was done with this. This is crazy and I still can't believe . . . I just can't believe she escaped from jail."

"Well, she did. You really need to watch your back, until we can get her back in custody. I talked to her face-to-face. I saw madness in her eyes. She's even more dangerous than she was before, because her lies were almost convincing."

He didn't have to tell me. I saw much madness in her eyes, too. I just had to make sure Eric had my back. It was a good thing that he didn't believe her. I had to make sure his thoughts about her didn't change.

"Don't fall for her bullshit again, E. You of all people know how she operates."

"I do, but please do not underestimate her."

"I won't. I get how sick she is—she needs to get some fucking help. How was she able to get away again, if you realized who she was?"

"At first, I wasn't sure. But as she kept talking to me, something eerie inside of me was going on. I kept studying her features. There was something about her slightly pointed nose that I remembered. If you recall, she and I had gotten real close. I remember her well, and all the cosmetic surgery in the world wouldn't make me forget Abigail Wilson."

I was completely speechless. Now, I felt like the fool. Why hadn't I noticed what Eric had, especially since I had spent so much time with Abby in the past? This was scary. I wished I had killed that bitch. She was trying to set me up, and there was no telling who she'd been talking to.

"I can't believe we're sitting here having this conversation about Abby. And to think that she tricked me out of all that money, E, I am sick. I can tell you this. If she keeps coming around playing these games with me, I'm going to hurt her. I'm a very nice guy, but Abby is going to push me to the edge."

"I can't say I blame you one bit. But just know that I'm going to do my job and find her. She needs to be back in jail where she belongs."

"I couldn't agree with you more."

Just as Eric was about to leave, April showed up at my door in her cheerleading uniform. Pom-poms were in her hands and her hair was in a sleek ponytail. I wasn't even sure why she wore her uniform, because she had been kicked off the team. Regardless, her timing couldn't be worse. I was afraid she would say something that she had no business saying. She was real rude.

"Let me know when you're done, because I need to talk to you. Now, so hurry it the hell up."

Eric stood with thick wrinkles lining his forehead. He appeared to be in disbelief. He looked at April, then back at me. "Please don't tell me these kids are this disrespectful these days. Really?"

"Hey, out of control, man, completely out of control. I'm surprised you don't see it on the streets. You have no idea what I go through as the school counselor. The teachers, however, have it much worse than I do."

"Yes, I do catch hell on the streets, but you can keep this job. At least I know how to deal with people who get out of control like this. That shit is crazy."

Eric mean mugged April as he walked out the door. She rolled her eyes at him, and as soon as I went to the door and locked it, I reached for the back of her ponytail, yanking it. Her head was pulled back, and even though she had beautiful brown skin, I could see her face turning red.

"Don't you ever fucking talk to me like that! Do, you, understand!"

"Ooooouch," she said, trying to pull away from me. "Let my hair go, nigga!"

I pulled tighter, before shoving her ass against the wall. Now wasn't the time or place to fuck with me. This situation with Abby had me on edge. I was ready to hurt somebody, and since April wanted to act like she was ignorant, she was right on time. I pointed my finger at her face—it took everything I had not to punch her.

"I got your nigga. If you keep it up, I'mma show him to you every time I see you. Now get the hell out of my office. Don't say shit else to me. I'm done with you."

I shoved April away from me. She almost fell, but managed to keep her balance. Tears were in her eyes as she stormed out of my office like a madwoman. I just didn't get how some women played the victims, when they were the ones who started shit. I wasn't worried about her one bit. In the eyes of many, she was just another troubled girl, seeking attention. She'd been in a mountain of trouble at school, and her whack mama didn't even give a damn. As for her father, who knew where he was?

I left work that day, watching my back as Eric had suggested. Something told me Abby had been watching me. I knew how she moved, and as I'd thought more about it, I sat in my car and called Toya. I'd already called Shanelle who disappeared from my apartment a few weeks ago. She'd left, without saying a single word or leaving me a text message. I hadn't heard from her since, and when I called, she never answered. I'd thought it was strange. Maybe Abby had something to do with it.

"What?" Toya snapped. "I know you ain't calling me, are you? You must have the wrong number."

"Nah, I got the right number. I'm calling because I miss you. I've been thinking about you lately, and I'm disappointed that you haven't returned to school yet."

"You didn't seem too disappointed during our last conversation. As a matter of fact, your exact words were for me to stay the fuck away from you, wasn't it?"

"That's because I was upset with you. Whether you realize it or not, Toya, you caused me a lot of setbacks. I wasn't ready to go at it with my wife like that, and she almost killed me. You can't expect me to be happy about that."

"I guess not, but what you said to me was foul. As for school, I'm already working on getting my GED. I want to stay as far away from you as possible. There's too much shit going on, and from what I heard, you've been messing around with a whole lot of people's heads."

It appeared that Toya had been talking to someone. In order to get more information from her, I had to approach this the right way. I invited her over to my place.

"I don't have my car. It broke down on me last week and I don't have any money yet to fix it."

"I'll give you the money to get it fixed. I'm on my way to get you, so be ready when I get there."

She didn't respond, so I called her name.

"Did you hear what I said? Why aren't you saying anything?"

"Because Brent. I don't want to keep playing this game with you. I'm scared and you don't know what it's like to—"

"You don't have to be scared of anything, alright? We're just two people who enjoy being around each other. What's so wrong with that?"

"Nothing, but wha . . . what about our age difference? I'm only eighteen. There's a big age difference between us."

"So. When has that ever mattered to you? What does age have to do with anything? We're two mature adults who are capable of making sound decisions. I'm surprised that you brought that up. Have you been talking to someone?"

She got quiet again. I already knew the answer; therefore, I had to hurry up and do what I needed to turn things around.

CHAPTER TWELVE

The glee I'd felt from kicking Brent's ass was starting to wear off. I'd left Jeff's place and had been back at my apartment for the past two days, trying to figure out what to do next. I suspected that Eric had already reached out to Brent and told him everything. He now knew who I was, and that was a game changer. For whatever reason, I felt like I needed to let Eric know what was up. Instead of going to see him, I'd mailed him the photos I'd found at Brent's place. Maybe, just maybe, he'd do the right thing and start doing a little digging on his own. It didn't take much for me to find out, and anybody who cared could figure out exactly what Brent had been up to.

As I waited for Jeff to bring me something to eat, I paced the floor in the living room. My cellphone was in my hand and I took a deep breath, before dialing Kendal's cellphone number. I said I wasn't going to call her, but I just wanted to hear her voice. I wanted to know how my grandson was doing, and maybe I'd get a chance to say hello to him. To my surprise, when I punched in her number, a young male picked up. I didn't know who it was, until he said his name was Micah. I felt relieved.

"Hi, Micah. This is Kendal's mother, Abby. Is she around? Do you mind if I speak to her?"

The call instantly dropped. I looked at my phone, thinking it was the battery, but it was fully charged. Maybe something was wrong with his phone, so I punched in the number, again, and called back. This time, the phone went to voicemail.

"Micah, I don't know what happened, but for some reason the call ended. Will you please tell my daughter I called and ask her to call me back. I just want to check on her. I know she's probably heard some unfortunate news about me, but I want her to know the truth and hear it from me. Okay. I hope all is good with you and thanks for being her support system. Kiss my babies for me."

An hour had gone by and I still hadn't heard anything from Kendal or Micah. I hadn't heard from Jeff either, and when I called to see about my food, he went off on me.

"Look, you gon' have to call DoorDash or something. I'm too busy right now, and with that Beyoncé concert coming tomorrow night, you know these hoes up in here trying to get dolled up. I'm surprised you don't want to go."

"I don't have time for no concert right now. If I did, I would be more interested in going to see Jill Scott or my girl, H.E.R."

"Well, good luck with that cause Bey is the shits. I'll be there tomorrow night, and my tickets are right up front. When Beyoncé get a look at my pretty ass, I know she gon' pull me right on that stage with her."

"I'm sure she will. Have fun and let me call DoorDash to see if I can get some food delivered. I'm hungry as hell."

"Okay, Sweet Pea. I'm glad you're feeling better. If I don't see you tomorrow, I'll see you in a few days. Keep the doors locked and stay away from Brent."

That's what I intended to do, but so many thoughts swarmed in my head. I hadn't been following him at all, because I feared what he would do to me to retaliate. Did he or did he not know who I was? Was it now time for me to kill him, surrender and go back to jail? I just didn't know, and I hated waiting around for Eric to do the right thing and investigate Brent.

After I finished half of the pizza that was delivered, I chilled in the bedroom, watching TV. The room was kind of stuffy, and I just couldn't seem to get more air to come out of the vents. I turned the ceiling fan on high, fluffed the thick body pillow that was behind me and sat against the headboard. The long pajama top I wore had a big lip print on the front, and my hair was tied down with a scarf. I was bored with the reality TV show I was watching; my mind kept drifting. The second Kendal crossed my mind again, I reached for my phone to call her. Yet again, Micah answered the phone.

"Micah, did you get my message?"

"Who dis?" he said, sounding playful.

"This is Abby, Kendal's mother. Is she there?"

"Hell, nah, that bitch ain't here. Stop calling my phone, au'ight?'

He hung up on me. To say I was shocked would be an understatement. My mouth was wide open; my whole face was tight. Why did he call her a bitch, and what did he mean by she wasn't there? She had to be there. She had to be with him. Maybe I had the wrong number. Or maybe he was high and was just playing with me. I didn't know what in the hell was going on, so I quickly called him back to inquire. Thankfully, he answered again.

"Listen, and don't you dare hang up on me. Where in the hell is Kendal? I need to speak to her now. I want to speak to my grandson, and you need to stop playing this damn game with me."

"Ain't nobody playing no game with you. You need to stop playing these games with me. I said quit calling my phone. Your daughter is not here. If or whenever you see that bitch, tell her I'mma bust her upside the head for lying on me."

I swear I almost died when he hung up on me again. What in the hell was going on? I needed some answers. I needed to know where Micah was, but how in the heck was I going to find him?

There I was at eleven o'clock at night, trying to replay the past in my head. Micah was Kendal's boyfriend. I thought she was pregnant by him. Then, Kendal told me while I was locked up that the baby was Brent's, but Micah was going to help her raise the baby as his. Maybe that's what he meant about her lying on him. Was he that upset with her? Did things not work out as planned? I needed to know something—now. Unfortunately, he was the only person who could tell me. I had to call him back and find out every single thing I could. He answered the phone and went off on me.

"Didn't I tell you to stop calling me? Damn, you just like yo crazy ass daughter! You don't listen and all I want is to be left the hell alone!"

"Micah, please!" I shouted. "Look, I don't know what's going on and I have no idea why you're talking that way. All I know is when Kendal came to see me in jail, she told me that you and her were together, raising my grandson. She told me about Brent raping her, but she said the two of you were moving away from St. Louis and starting over. Where are you and please, please, please tell me everything is okay with my daughter and grandson."

He laughed out loud. "Did she really tell you that bullshit? Man, that chick is whack. I can tell you this, au'ight? I'm still in St. Louis and I ain't never been nowhere else. Your daughter is a fucking liar. A big ass liar and that's only one of the reasons why we're not together."

By now, I was almost ready to pass out. My heart was racing, palms were sweating and I couldn't get the right words to come out of my mouth. "Wha . . . what exactly did she lie about? Where is my grandson? Is Kendal still in St. Louis?"

"She lies about everything."

"Everything like what?" I shouted and damn near busted my own eardrum.

"I'll let her tell you, and text you her address. As for your grandchild, she lost our baby. Or should I say, our child died two months after he was born. I don't even know if he was mine. She lied about that, too, and I've been done with her ass ever since."

Micah hung up. I fell back on the bed, feeling numb. I was hurt and confused as ever as I waited for him to send me Kendal's address. When he did, tears rained from my eyes. I was crushed, could barely catch my breath. Felt humiliated and damn near wanted to die, right then and there. I fell to my knees, asking God why he had been so cruel to me. What in the hell did I do to deserve all of this? This couldn't be happening to me, and why,

why, why did it have to be like this? It took a while for me to gather myself. When I did, it wasn't until, at least, three in the morning. I was so weak and very sick to my stomach. My head was banging, and every time I looked at the address Micah had sent me, I was in total disbelief. There was no way in hell Kendal had been living at that address. No way in the devil's lonely hell.

CHAPTER THIRTEEN

BRENT CARSON

After I picked up Toya and took her to a Chinese restaurant, I stopped at the ATM machine to get some cash. I gave her three hundred dollars to get her car fixed. She was very happy about that.

"Thank you," she said, tucking the money away in her purse. "You're always so sweet and nice when you want to be. But don't think I've forgotten about how you treated me."

I reached over and rubbed Toya's smooth leg. She was probably one of the prettiest girls in the world, but annoying at times. Her long, natural hair flowed midway down her back, and her brown skin was blemish free. With light-brown eyes, and a body sculptured like a goddess, it was so easy for me to be attracted to her. I liked that she was a little on the wild side, but then there was a side of her that was real reserved. Of course she was head over heels for me; I liked her a lot as well. She just messed up when she contacted Lajuanna. I couldn't forgive her, until now. Now, I needed to know if she'd been running her mouth to anyone. Hopefully, for her sake, she'd tell me the truth.

"I apologized to you, didn't I?" I said. "Promised I'd make it up to you and everything. Just don't be mad at me. You know I don't like it when you're mad at me. You aren't still mad at me, are you?"

Toya blushed. Her smile warmed my heart. She was so sweet. Sweet and extremely crazy about me.

"I don't know yet. It depends."

"Depends on what?"

"Depends on when we get to your place, how well you treat me."

I chuckled and hurried to get home. As soon as we stepped in the door, I had Toya wrapped in my arms. My fingers were gripped in her hair as we kissed, and she was on the tips of her toes, trying to suck in as much of my tongue as she could. Her tongue was pierced—my dick got harder and harder as I thought about how skilled her head game was.

"You," I said between sloppy, wet kisses. "I guess you're not going to give me time to get out of this suit, are you?"

"Nope."

She was giddy as ever. She threw her arms around my neck and started to undo my tie. I hiked her pretty ass up to my hips and carried her right over to the kitchen counter. After I placed her on it, she ripped my shirt open and pulled my jacket away from my broad shoulders.

"You're being awfully aggressive with me," I teased. "Just so you know, I love it. Every bit of it, baby."

I sucked on her neck while holding her sexy hips. My shirt and jacket hit the floor, and as she yanked my belt away from my slacks, I removed her t-shirt. She didn't have on a bra, so I was able to tackle her firm titties first. The second I covered her breast with my mouth, she rushed to lower my slacks. They dropped to the floor, and after I scooted her closer to me, I moved her silk panties aside and slipped my steel right into her folds. The feel of her tight walls suffocating my dick drove me nuts. I started wearing her ass out, and as I pounded her insides, she kept pushing my chest back, trying to back away from me.

"Don't run from it now," I said. "Woman up. You can handle this."

"You'd better know I caaaaaan," she moaned. "All day, every day."

Those were fighting words to me. I had to show her who the boss was. I did so when I leaned her over the counter and held her head down. Her feet barely touched the floor, and as I slammed my meat into her, churning her insides until it melted like butter, she went crazy. She cried out my name while calling me all kinds of motherfuckers.

"You ain't shit! I swear you ain't shit, but keep beating this pussy niggaaaaa! Kill this shit and suck up every ounce I'm about to give you!"

Toya's explosion was quite impressive. My whole shaft dripped with her fluids, and instead of me washing her up with my mouth, she dropped to her knees and took the initiative to clean me first. My legs were so weak that I held on to the counter to keep my balance. My head was dropped back, and with my eyes shut tight, I softly thanked Toya for being so good to me.

"That's right, baby. Treat it how you want to be treated. Take your time and make Daddy feel special."

Toya delivered. She kept telling me how much she had missed me; I believed her. I thanked her again as we cuddled in my bed. A cigar dangled from the corner of my mouth, and while one of her legs was crossed over my legs, she was vaping. I finally asked her if anybody had come around asking about me. Instead of answering, she circled her finger around my nipple, trying to get me roweled up again. I removed the cigar, placed it in an ashtray and then grabbed her wrist to stop her.

"Did you hear my question? Answer me, Toya. And tell me the truth."

She snatched her wrist away from my grip and toyed with my nipple again. "The truth is, somebody did come to my house and question me about you."

"When and who was it?" I rushed to say.

"I think it was last week or the week before. It was a real pretty lady who said you'd done something to her daughter. She tried to insinuate that I was too young and gullible to be with you. When she mentioned getting you arrested, I shut her down and made her leave."

I was disappointed that Toya had even spoken to Abby. I also wasn't sure if Toya was being truthful with me about telling Abby to leave. While I knew Toya was wrapped around my finger, something wasn't adding up.

"Describe how the woman you spoke to looked," I said. "And what specifically did you say to her?"

"If I can recall, she had short hair that was slicked down on the sides. Her skin was light brown and her eyes were like gray or green. She was real slim, and she drove a Volkswagen. All she griped about was her daughter and how you and me shouldn't be in a relationship. Do you know who she was?"

"Yes, she's a hater. I didn't do anything to her daughter. She's just bitter because I broke it off with her. She found out about us, and I guess she's trying to stir up more trouble by getting you to go against me."

Toya shook her head and rolled her eyes. "That's so messed up. I'm glad that I told her I wanted nothing to do with her plans. I made it clear that I wasn't going to say a word to anybody about us. She pretended like she really cared about me, but I figured something was up. I guess I should've called and told you about her visit. Actually, I wanted to, but I knew how upset you were with me. I just didn't feel like arguing again."

I kissed her forehead and rubbed her backside. "You did the right thing. Thanks, baby. If anybody ever comes around asking questions about us, be sure to let me know."

"I sure will," she said, straddling her legs on top of me. I held her small waist as she rolled the smoke around in her mouth and started to ground her hips. She was ready to crank up the engine again.

"You'd better stop that shit," I said. "You gon' make me give you some babies."

She laughed and positioned my package to enter her. "One or two babies?" she asked.

"Fiiiiive," I grunted as the ride had started to get rocky. "Shit, maybe six."

She laughed again and refused to let me get any sleep. By the time I showered and got dressed for work in the morning, she was knocked out. I was somewhat worried, especially since I now knew Abby had been in touch with some people. I had to shut things down for a while just in case Eric started doing a little snooping. I quietly made my way to the kitchen and called Karla. I asked her if anyone had reached out to her. She said no.

"Are you sure?" I pushed.

"I'm sure. No one has called me to say anything about you. If they did, I would tell you."

"Please do. In the meantime, I think we need to chill for a while. Maybe you should spend more time with your husband and see if the two of you can work things out."

"I have no plans to work things out with him, and I know you're not trying to end this with me, especially after I gave you that money. Is that what this is all about?"

"No, it's not. I will pay the money back, soon. As for us, I think its best that we chill for a while. I have a lot on my plate. My job is keeping me busy and I'm thinking about coaching the boys' basketball team. I might not have much time to see you."

"Yeah, whatever, Brent. You know I'm not the kind of woman who will clown on you for this, but please make sure you give me the funds to pay on that loan. It's due on the 15th of every month. I expect to see or hear from you then."

"No doubt. Thanks again and I'll be in touch."

Karla sounded disappointed, but I always knew that she wasn't really into me like some of the other women were. All she wanted was sex. Sex with no ties. Our relationship was easy.

I finished my coffee then left. With the leather backpack on my shoulder, I stood for a moment, checking my surroundings. I wondered when Abby would show her face again. It would be just a matter of time. This time, though, I'd be better prepared.

CHAPTER FOURTEEN

At five o'clock in the morning, while in a complete daze, I slowly drove to the address Micah had given me. I had hoped it wasn't the exact same apartment complex I had followed Brent to, but unfortunately it was. I had referred to this chick as his late-night side ho. I'd never seen the woman's face, but now I knew that the person inside was Kendal. Brent had been coming over here, spending the night with her. There was a lot to unpack with this, and I damn sure didn't know everything yet. Maybe I was missing something. Maybe he was trying to be there for his son, but then again, Micah said there was no baby. If there wasn't, who was the boy Kendal had brought to the jail to see me? He surely resembled Brent to me. They had the same birthmark, too, but was this all a plan to confuse or hurt me? I surely hoped not. I prayed that wasn't the case. Kendal would be able to unpack all of this for me, for sure.

Instead of getting out of the car, I parked on the other side of the parking lot and waited. I returned Jeff's Volkswagen to him, and asked him if I could use his Ford Fusion instead. Brent was very familiar with the kind of car I drove; I didn't want him to see the same Volkswagen. I predicted he would be making his way over here, soon, so I patiently waited. I waited for Kendal to do her thing, too. I wanted to watch her movements and examine her demeanor. Would she appear happy or sad? I was fearful of just going to her apartment and knocking on the door. But if it came to that, I most certainly would. She wouldn't recognize the *new* me. She hadn't a clue what I looked like, but I had to wonder if Brent had already told her. More so, had Officer Wayne already told him? For starters, that's what I needed to know. I reached for my phone, while my eyes were still focused on Kendal's apartment. When an officer answered the phone, I spoke up.

"Hello. I'm trying to reach Officer Eric Wayne. I was in a car accident yesterday and I'm trying to get the report for my insurance company. Is he available?"

"I'm not sure. I think he already left, but let me check."

"Thanks."

I waited and squinted as I saw two people leaving an apartment. It wasn't Kendal. I felt relieved, until I heard Eric's voice on the phone.

"Officer Wayne speaking."

"Hi. It's me. I know you already know who me is, so I don't have to be specific. I need you to investigate Brent. Do it now, before it's too late. Talk to Toya Ferguson, April Carter and my daughter, Kendal. I will send you their addresses. Go to that school and ask around to see if there are more girls accusing Brent of rape. Do it, Eric. Do your job, and more than anything, talk to Brent. Have you spoken to him already?"

"I surely have, and you know what, Abby? He's going to kill you. He's sick of this and so am I. You need to turn yourself in. You need to stop this and get the help you need. This isn't going to end well for you. I can promise you that."

His words and refusal to do anything angered me. I swallowed the huge lump in my throat and tried to convince him that he was making a mistake.

"I know you think I'm crazy, and after what I did, I would think so too. But what I did was make some horrible mistakes and bad choices. What Brent is doing is bigger than that. He's dangerous. You shouldn't be protecting him. I'm begging you to follow up, and did you get the photos I sent you? I sent them the other day. You should have them by now."

His voice went up a notch. "Listen, I got people out here killing each other. I got churches being blown up, and drive-by shootings happening every day. Just yesterday, one of my officers was killed in the line of duty. He'd been here for almost twenty years, and was shot down in front of his wife and children. Do you think I got time for your fucking games? Hell, no, I don't so please stop this nonsense and leave that man alone. It's over, Abby, damn! Why can't you get that through your thick head? Brent just wants to be left alone. So do I, and my advice to you, again, would be to turn yourself in and end this."

Truly disappointed, I ended the call. There was no getting through to Eric. He was going to defend Brent until the end. At least I now knew, for sure, that he'd already told Brent who I was. I really had to be more careful. If not, he was right. This wasn't going to end well for me.

For the next hour or so, I sat in the car, listening to music. People were going in and out of the apartment complex, but I hadn't seen Kendal yet. I wasn't even sure if she was in there, but when night time came, I saw the lights come on. I could see someone walking around, but it was only a shadow behind the curtains. I kept wondering if I should go to the door or not. It would take me a minute to explain why I was there and why I appeared so different. After one more hour in the car, I was ready to confront her. That was until I saw Brent's car pull into a parking spot. The second he got out, I saw him looking around. His hands were in his pockets; he even paused for a minute to light a cigar. Then, he walked slowly to the apartment where Kendal was. I saw him use a key to go inside, but I couldn't see much else after that. This was my chance to go see what was up. I didn't want anyone to see me, so I put on a hat, shielded my eyes with shades and threw on an oversized jacket. My tight jeans and tennis shoes were comfortable. I was able to creep up to the slide-in door and peek inside. The first person I spotted was Kendal. My heart went out to my baby. She was so beautiful as she stood in the tiny kitchen with her arms folded. Her back was against the fridge, and all she was doing was listening. Listening to Brent as he stood closer to the door, saying something. He kept darting his finger and wiping across his lips. I didn't see any children. The apartment showed no signs of a child being there, but I was happy to see my baby. She looked so mature. Her hair was in a neat bun, and wavy baby-hair rested along her hairline. Her eyes were just like mine— big and bold. Thick lashes made them appear bigger and her girlie figure was no more. With gray sweatpants on and a crop top that displayed her midriff, she was what I considered Brent's type. That was beautiful, fatherless, gullible, seeking any kind of love and very vulnerable.

As he moved closer to her, my heart sank. My hands started to tremble and my eyes focused without a blink. He kept talking, and in the midst of him saying something, Kendal laughed. She actually laughed. She then lifted her hand and placed her finger over his lips. He smacked it away and said something else to her. After that, I couldn't even watch the two of them anymore. The kiss was heartbreaking. It sent me running away from the door, falling on my ass as I tripped down some steps, while wiping my tears along the way. How in the hell had this happened? When did it happen and how could I have been so foolish and blind? My stomach hurt so bad—by the time I reached the car, I had to throw the fuck up. I was bent over beside the car, gagging and spitting uncontrollably. I didn't even notice the man who had gotten out of his car to ask if I was okay.

"Can I get you something?" he asked from a few feet away. "Here, let me open the door to your car so you can sit down."

"No," I said, standing up straight while holding my stomach. I wiped across my mouth and took several deep breaths. "I'll be okay. Thanks, but you can go."

"Are you sure? You don't look well. I can call an ambulance for you."

"No, please. I'm fine. I just ate something that didn't sit right with me."

"Okay. The last time I saw that much vomit was when my wife was pregnant. Morning sickness tore her up, but when all was said and done, we had a healthy baby boy."

I couldn't say anything. What he'd said made me think. Think real hard about what Brent had done to me. I wasn't pregnant, was I? *Hell no!* I thought. I couldn't stop thinking about it all. I was a mess. A complete mess, and I had to get out of there fast. Like a bat out of hell, I rushed off the parking lot, damn near running over the man who was trying to help me. He jumped out of the way and yelled after me. I didn't even know what he'd said. All I wanted now was a pregnancy test. Thankfully, Walgreens was just a few minutes away. I jerked the car in park, rushed inside and snatched a pregnancy test from the shelf. Unfortunately, the line was long so I had to wait. My arms were crossed and I nervously patted my foot on the floor, waiting for people in line to hurry it the fuck up. One older lady was fumbling around with coins in her purse, trying to count them one by one. The man after her, his card was declined, so the cashier had to call a manager to cancel the transaction. By the time the cashier got to me, I just dropped money on the counter, snatched up the pregnancy test and rushed towards the restroom. I hurried to lower my jeans to my ankles, and as I squatted over the toilet, I peed on the stick. In less than a minute, it showed negative. I dropped to my knees and cried. Sobbed like a baby—this hurt so bad. All of it, and I couldn't stop blaming myself for letting a man like Brent slip into our lives. What in the hell was wrong with me? How did I let him get in? This was something I had to live with and it hurt like hell.

I left the stall, washed my hands and splashed cold water all over my face. Bags were underneath my eyes, and today, I looked as bad as I felt. I didn't want to drive back to the apartment, but I did. This time, the lights were out and Brent's car was still there. At that moment, I had a decision to make. Should I go to the door, clown on their asses or wait? I pondered for a few minutes. Minutes that seemed like an hour. An hour that seemed too long, so I finally started the car back up and left.

CHAPTER FIFTEEN

OFFICER ERIC WAYNE

I loved my job, but I'd be the first to admit that it was no picnic. Lately, it seemed like things were spiraling out of control in my jurisdiction and things had gone from bad to worse. We did whatever we could to stop the bleeding. We were trying to make inroads with a community that didn't trust us, felt like they couldn't rely on us and refused to work with us. It was a bad and unfortunate situation. Things had gone down for years, but I was doing my best to show up and prove to people in the community that I really did care.

What I didn't care about was Abby and her foolishness. I'd gotten the envelope she'd sent and tossed it right in the trash. She had already wasted enough of my time before. Last time it was worth it, because we knew she was plotting to kill people. It was my job to protect people, so we created a masterplan to set her up and put her behind bars for a long while. This time, it wasn't worth it because I knew how much she still loved Brent. As mad as she was, she would never kill him. She was too obsessed with him. All I had to do was find her and put her in jail again. If Brent got to her before I did, so be it.

The day had already been chaotic when we received notification that a student at Hazelwood High had entered the building with a gun and was threatening students. Many people were on edge; the situation was fluid. The whole parking lot was swarmed with concerned parents; police vehicles and teachers had already started to rush some of the students out of the building. By the time I got inside, the student was already in handcuffs and under control in the principal's office. I was shocked to see that the student was the same person I had crossed paths with the day I was in Brent's office. She sat in the chair, unbothered, with her head up high while chewing gum. Her eyes kept rolling, and whenever the principal said anything to her, she wouldn't answer.

"I just don't know the reason for all of this," the principal said, frustrated, while trying to explain something even he didn't understand. "I've tried to get April to talk and her mother has already been notified. I don't know what else to do. We've done everything to try and prevent incidents like these from happening."

"We'll take it from here," I said.

In an effort not to make a bigger scene, I told the other officers to clear the entire school. The principal was asked to send the students home, and we waited until the buses came to pick them up. While we waited, I spoke to a few lingering students who told me how April's behavioral problems led to her getting kicked off the cheerleading squad and suspended one time for cursing at a teacher. I had witnessed the way she'd spoken to Brent, and I looked around to see if I could find him. He wasn't in his office, so I figured he was somewhere doing everything he could to protect the other students.

As things started to settle down a little, I left the building to go park my car around the back. It wouldn't look right to bring April out the front door in handcuffs, and the media was right outside waiting so they could blast what had happened on the news. That wasn't going to happen. I made it clear to the other officers, who stood in the office with me, to make sure the coast was clear.

"Let's go young lady," I said to April. She stood and didn't say one word as I escorted her toward the back exit with her hands cuffed behind her back. Without anyone seeing me, I placed her in the police vehicle and drove off. I figured the police station would be packed with journalists from the media. Sure enough, it was. This time, I drove through the underground parking garage and looked at April through the rearview mirror.

"You sure have garnered a lot of attention," I said. "I guess that was your purpose, huh?"

She ignored me and turned her head to look out the window. Minutes later, I removed her from the car and took her to a private room in the far back of the police station. I removed the handcuffs and asked if she wanted anything to eat or drink.

"Nope," she said, rubbing her wrist.

"We've already contacted your mother. She should be here shortly."

"Yeah, right. Good luck with that. I'll wait, but I won't hold my breath. Neither should you."

I wasn't sure if her mother was coming or not, but after thirty minutes had passed, I entered the room with a pack of Oreo cookies and an orange juice in my hand.

"I know you said you didn't want anything, but I figured you were hungry. This is all I could find. If you don't want it, I understand."

I sat across the table from her, then placed the items on it. She picked up the pack of Oreos and smiled.

"These are my favs," she said. "I can't touch that juice, though. I'm allergic to oranges."

"Got it. I'll go get you something to drink later, so you can wash down those cookies. Until then, tell me what happened today. Why did you bring a gun to school and threaten other students?"

Brenda Hampton

"Because people are so stupid. I hate some of those people and I just wanted to scare them."

"But why though? Have they been bullying you?"

"Some of them were, but that don't really bother me as much. I just hate when people gossip, particularly when they don't really know nothing about me."

"So, you were mad because they were gossiping about you? I heard you were removed from the cheerleading team. Were they gossiping about that?"

"Yeah, they gossiped about that and said I wasn't good enough to be on the team. Just a whole lot of stuff that was starting to work my nerves."

Teenagers were so fragile. Everything was such a big deal to them. It was so easy for them to get their feelings hurt. Unfortunately, that's what this was about. I felt bad, too, because jail or a detention center was her next stop.

"If or whenever someone works your nerves, as you say, you need to speak up. Bringing a gun to school was the wrong thing to do. You scared a lot of people and you already know how bad many of these situations have turned out. I wish you would've spoken to someone about how you felt about the gossiping. It's important that you open up and not let your troubles fester. There are plenty of good teachers you could have spoken to, and didn't I see you meeting with your counselor the other day? I was in Mr. Carson's office when you showed up that day."

She looked at me and bit into her bottom lip. "Yeah, I remember seeing you."

"I remember you well. Why were you so upset that day?"

She shrugged while opening the cookie bag. "I don't want to talk about it."

"Why not? I want you to talk about it, because I need to do everything I can to help you. It's okay if I help you, isn't it?"

"Let's be real, okay? You're not trying to help me. Don't nobody want to help, and damn sure not Brent."

"Brent? You mean, Mr. Carson. You're not on a first-name basis with the school counselor, are you?"

"Everybody calls him that. I just call him Brent and an asshole sometimes."

I didn't want to push, especially since she seemed to be opening up to me. But as I sat there thinking about what Abby had said, I remembered her telling me to talk to April Carter. April Carter was now sitting across from me. I scratched my head, approaching this with ease.

"Asshole," I said, laughing. "Why are you calling the school counselor an asshole? He couldn't be that bad, is he?"

While taking a bite of the cookie, she examined me. I didn't want to make our conversation all about Brent, but I needed her to talk.

"Nah, he ain't that bad," she admitted.

"Then why did you call him an asshole?"

"Because many of the teachers at my school are assholes. Not just him."

"Yeah, back in the day, I felt the same way. I disliked many of my teachers. I only felt a connection with one or two of them. They were the nice ones. The ones who seemed to really care. I could go to them and talk about anything. My counselor actually reminded me of Brent. She was a good listener, and she was the reason why I decided to be a police officer."

"Brent is a good listener too. A lot of us like him, especially the girls."

I chuckled and kept the conversation going. "The girls, huh? That must mean y'all think he's pretty attractive."

She smiled. I saw glee in her eyes as she talked about him. "Naaaah, fine as fuck. He pretty dope. Yeah, he dope."

"That's good. A dope asshole. I've never heard it put like that before."

She laughed and bit into the cookie again. "Well, you know how we young folks do it. Anyway, do you mind getting me something to drink? My throat is dry and I want to know if my mother arrived yet."

"Sure, no problem." I stood up. "Is a Pepsi okay? I think we got Sierra Mist in the machines too."

"Sierra Mist is fine. Thanks."

I walked to the door, but before I opened it, I turned to her again. "April, tell me something, okay? And be real honest with me. You know it's important for you to be honest with me, right?"

"Yeah, I know. What's up?"

"Did Mr. Carson have anything to do with why you brought that gun to school today? Were you upset with him about something, something you would like to tell me about?"

She slumped in the chair and folded her arms across her chest. "He didn't have anything to do with it. I told you why I brought the gun to school. I wanted to stop the gossiping and put fear in the kids who were starting rumors."

Again, I didn't want to push so I thanked her and left the room. Something didn't sit well with me, but I couldn't figure out what it was. Even when I went back into the room and talked to April for another hour or so, she gave me nothing. The fact that she purposely avoided my questions about Brent bothered me. I read people very well, and once I was done talking to her, I didn't have a good feeling about none of this.

The following day, I went back to Hazelwood High to chat with Brent again. He was on his way into a meeting and reminded me that he didn't have much time to talk. While he was sitting on the edge of his desk, I stood by the door. I told him how difficult it was for me to arrest April.

"I couldn't believe it," Brent said, wiping his shiny head. "I know she had some problems, but I never thought she was the kind of girl who would do something like that."

"It's funny you would say that because everybody I spoke to yesterday said she was troubled. They mentioned her being kicked off the cheerleading team and said she'd cussed out a teacher."

"I know all about that, man, but we shouldn't judge these kids by a few incidents they had. Many of them are just messed up because their parents don't support them and they're not required to follow any rules. I see it all day, every day. I just try to be there for them as much as I can. April came to my office, numerous times. We had plenty of discussions about how she was feeling and what she wanted to do in the future. I really tried to encourage her to do the right thing and stay on the right path. What she did yesterday surprised me. She's a good kid, E, and I really hope you can do whatever you can to minimize her punishment. Can you do that for me?"

I walked up to Brent and slapped my hand against his. "I'll do whatever I can do and let you know."

"Thanks, my brother. By the way, have you heard anything else from Abby?"

I was going to tell him I had, but decided not to. He already had enough to worry about. "Not a word. If I do, you know I'll be in touch."

"Cool," he said.

We left his office together, laughing about baseball practice. I felt better after our conversation, and was a little disappointed in myself for letting Abby get to me. *Shame on me*, I thought. *Shame on me for listening to her lies.*

CHAPTER SIXTEEN

I couldn't hold back any longer. Today was the day I was going to confront Kendal. I'd been watching her from a distance, and every time I wanted to say something to her, I couldn't. I purposely bumped into her at the mall the other day. She bought a purse at Macy's, and I was in the store with her. She didn't even recognize me. I stood right next to her, but she never looked my way. I followed her to the food court where she ate with one of her friends. Afterwards, they went to a movie and then parted ways. Kendal returned home, but Brent didn't show up that night or the next night. The day after that, he did. As usual, it was late. He stayed the night and went to work in the morning. This was their routine. Not once did I see them leave the apartment together. It was as if Kendal was always there, waiting for him to show up. She wasn't working, so I didn't know how she'd gotten the money to pay rent or shop. The apartment complex she lived in wasn't a hole in the wall. It was nice. Kind of upscale, and she seemed happy to be here.

Another thing . . . there was no child. None whatsoever. I couldn't wait to ask her about the child she'd told me was my grandson. I needed answers, and as I knocked on the door to the apartment, holding my breath, I expected to get the answers I needed. She opened the door wide enough so I could see her.

"Yes," she said, looking me up and down.

"Kendal."

"Who wants to know?"

"I know you don't recognize me, but I'm your mother."

Right then, she tried to shut the door in my face. I pushed back on the door; it was a struggle to keep it open.

"Stop, before I call the police," she yelled. "I have nothing to say to you! Go back where you came from!"

Her words were like a hard punch to my gut. I kept pushing on the door—had no intentions of giving up.

"I can't go. Please, Kendal, let's just talk. I know everything. Just about everything, so there's nothing else to hide!"

I overpowered her and managed to rush my way inside. By then, Kendal had her cellphone in her hand.

"Who are you calling?" I yelled. "Brent? Are you going to tell him I'm here?"

"No. I'm calling the police. I don't want you here. You should've never come here!"

I rushed up and snatched the phone from her hand. It fell on the floor and I kicked it underneath the fridge. She looked at me with so much hatred in her eyes. Her fist tightened and as she lifted it, I quickly threw out a warning that made her pause.

"I promise you that if you strike me, Kendal, I will beat your fucking ass! I don't know what has gotten into you, don't know why you've lied to me like this, but I do know that I will not stand for you putting your hands on me. Put your fist down and tell me what the fuck is going on!"

She mean mugged me and lowered her fist. Her chest heaved in and out, and as I stood in front of her, she walked around me and plopped on the couch. She folded her arms across her chest, while pressing her foot against the glass table.

"What do you want?" she said, pouting.

I stood several feet away from her, feeling frustrated and evil eyeing her, too.

"What I want is the truth from you. Tell me how we got here. Stop lying to me and tell me why in the hell are you with Brent."

She moved her head from side-to-side as if she was annoyed and irritated by my questions.

"You know damn well how we got here. You're the one who had to have him. You're the one who chose him over me. How can you stand there and ask me that question when you're the one who was so obsessed with him."

I threw my hands up in the air. "Fine, okay. Now that you got that off your chest, answer my questions. When you get done answering those, I have plenty more because none of this, not one single thing, makes any sense to me."

"You said you knew everything, didn't you? That's what you just said, so what else do you want me to say?"

I was trying my best not to hurt her. I wanted to stay calm and listen to her, but this was so hard. She was talking to me like I was dirt. Like I didn't mean anything to her. That truly broke my heart. I lowered my voice, trying to make her understand why it was important for us to discuss this.

"I don't know everything," I admitted. "I don't understand any of this and I need you to tell me what's going on, Kendal. Start from the beginning and tell me what is going on with you and Brent."

She was blunt. "What does it look like, mother? I'm with Brent, I've been with Brent and there you have it."

Still trying to stay calm, I struggled to hold in my emotions and moved closer to the sofa where she was. "Okay, so you've been with Brent. For how long, Kendal? Do you have a child with him, and if so, where is the baby?"

She sighed and continued to speak with an attitude. "I guess I need to let you off the hook. Brent said I should do it, but whenever this day came, trust me, I wanted to spare your little feelings. Had you been paying attention like a good mother is supposed to do, you would've known that Brent and me had been fucking around the whole time you were with him. The only reason I griped about him was because I wanted you to end it with him, so he wouldn't have his cake and eat it too. You didn't give a damn about me, Mama. You treated my father like shit and that's why he stopped coming around. Brent gave me everything I needed. He was always there for me, and when your stupid self got locked up, he stepped up and became the man I needed him to be. As for the baby I had, I lost him two months after he was born. I was under too much stress and that's what happens when your mother abandons you. I don't know who the father of my child was, but the baby I brought to see you was my friend's son. I told you he looked like Brent and you believed me. If I told you Brent was Jesus, you would believe that too. You can be mad at me all you want to, but at the end of the day, you brought all of this on yourself."

I'd stopped breathing, right after she admitted to being with Brent at the same time I was. There was no doubt that my child was brainwashed, and Brent had convinced her that she meant the world to him. In that moment, I experienced a pain unlike anything I had ever felt before. My whole body was burning hot. My legs were shaking; I could feel my emotions about to boil over. I had no words. My lips felt glued together. My head was thumping because my poor child was just as sick in the head and confused as I was. She needed help. We needed help. There was no getting through this without it, but I couldn't offer her that help right now. I was too mad; I didn't want to say the wrong thing. I refused to push her away, so I just stood, looking at her with so much disappointment in my eyes.

"Your looks do not scare me," she said. "I suggest you not come back here again. If you do, mother, I will have to call the police. You need to go back to jail where you belong. That way, Brent and me can live our lives in peace."

Well, I'll be damned. There it was. She . . . they wanted peace. So did I. "You need help, Kendal. When I come back, I'll be able to share information about where you can get it from."

She stood and moved face-to face-with me. "No, you need help. I'm fine, and I'm not going to let you dictate my life or make any suggestions about what I need to do. What you need to do is get the fuck out of me and my man's home."

I got it. I now understood how some mothers and daughters just couldn't seem to have respect for each other and get along. I felt it, but when all was said and done, she was still my daughter. I backed up and moved in another direction so I could go. Kendal, however, didn't want me to leave in peace. She grabbed my arm, and the second she called me a "stupid bitch" I shoved her ass back on the sofa and caged her in so she wouldn't move. I then grabbed her face, squeezing it so tight that her cheeks turned red.

"When I leave here, you'd better think long and hard about everything you said to me. You'd better get on your fucking knees and ask God to save you from that monster you now believe is your hero. I can assure you that I'm coming back. I'll be back for sure, and when you see me again, all I want is an apology. A sincere apology and for you to tell me you're ready to seek the help you need."

I released her face, and couldn't even make it to the door, before she fired back.

"Fuc—"

This time, I swung around and rushed up to her. I yanked her hair so hard, pulling her to the ground. She was now on her knees, scratching at my hands so I would release the grip on her hair.

"Don't do this Kendal!" I shouted. "Please don't make me do it!"

Seeing how angry I was, Kendal kept quiet. She whimpered, but didn't say another word. I left without closing the door behind me. Rushed to my car and sped off. There was so much anger inside of me. I had to release it and clown on this nigga, again. I didn't care anymore, because the way I saw it, Brent had won. He had taken so much from me. So much, and there was nothing I could say or do to change that.

Knowing exactly where he was, I drove to Hazelwood High. Since security wouldn't let me inside, I marched straight to his car that was parked on the parking lot. I used another bat I'd had in my trunk for protection, and went to town on his car. I swung the bat with all my might. Broke his windows, put numerous dents all over it and banged up his rims.

"You, lousy, motherfucker!" I shouted after every strike. "I, fucking, hate, you!"

The aluminum bat did everything I needed it to do, and it didn't break like the wooden one. Shattered glass was everywhere. His alarm was going off; it was a matter of time before someone came to stop me. Sweat dripped from my forehead as I jumped in my car. My arms were sore from swinging the bat so hard. I still didn't feel good about anything, but what was done was done.

CHAPTER SEVENTEEN

BRENT CARSON

I couldn't wait to get my hands on Abby, and was mad as hell when I ran outside and saw what she had done to my car. It was destroyed. I couldn't even drive it and glass was all over the parking lot. So many people were outside; it was embarrassing. The police had already arrived, and I yelled at two security guards who were supposed to monitor the school's parking lot.

"So, let me get this straight," I said, wiping across my sweaty forehead. "Anybody can just come on school premises, do this shit, drive off and get away with it? Why didn't nobody see her? Why couldn't she be stopped? This is crazy. I need her arrested, and why isn't nobody putting forth more effort to stop her?"

I looked at Eric who was writing something on a notepad. "We're stepping up our efforts to find her. No worries, and I'm truly sorry about your car."

"Me too, Mr. Carson," a security officer said. "I wasn't sure what was going on. Car alarms go off all the time on the parking lot. When it didn't stop, that's when I realized something was wrong and followed up on it."

"It shouldn't have taken that long," I shot back. "My car was parked in the front of this building. With all those windows and the doors being right there, there's no way she should've gotten away with this."

"I agree," Eric added. "Not to mention there are security cameras all over the place. You all have to do better than this. There needs to be someone monitoring those cameras at all times. No ifs, ands, or buts about it."

The security guard defended himself, along with another guard who was supposed to monitor the cameras. "Normally, we do watch them. But when I got called to the main office, several parents came in and Craig had to make sure they got passes. We were only away from the cameras for no more than five minutes. That was it, but I guess the timing didn't help."

"No, it didn't." I cut my eyes at him and reached for my cellphone to see if I could have a rental car sent to me. After going back and forth with the representative on the phone, she told me a car would arrive within thirty minutes to an hour. I then called a tow truck company to come pick up my car. The driver was there in less than fifteen minutes. After he drove away with my car, I stood outside talking to Eric.

"This shit is getting out of hand," I said to him. "Do you have any idea, whatsoever, where Abby might be?"

"Well, we damn sure know she's close by. While I would like for us to come up with another plan to set her up, I don't want you to find yourself in any trouble. Let me handle everything this time. I'll get her, I promise. Sooner or later, I'll get her. This time, she'll be sent away for good."

His words were like music to my ears. I needed something to happen soon, because I felt like Abby was getting too close to certain things people didn't need to know. Eric had already been asking too many questions. He seemed to be digging a little more than usual, and when he brought up April's name, it really concerned me.

"Her court date is set for three weeks from now," he said. "I don't know what the judge is going to decide, but I put in a good word for her, like you asked me to."

"Good, good," I said, keeping the conversation short.

"Maybe you should talk to the judge as well. It's always good to send a letter about a person's character so the judge can kind of get a clear picture. I'm sure April would appreciate you doing that for her."

"I'll think about it, but if you don't mind me saying, I have other things on my mind right now."

He grabbed my shoulder and squeezed it. "I understand. But don't let Abby frustrate you too much. You know this is how she operates. You can't let her win."

I agreed. When the rental car arrived, I left to go see Kendal. I knew how to get to Abby, without even seeing her. It was through her daughter. If Abby had been following me, I wanted to piss her off. Something had pissed her off for sure. I didn't find out what it was until I stood in the kitchen with Kendal. She told me Abby had stopped by earlier. I had already warned Kendal to be on the lookout for her.

"I told her everything," Kendal admitted. "She needed to know. Maybe she will now be able to move on and leave us alone."

"I doubt that. Besides, you know your mother better than I do. She's crazy. Crazy people don't stop until they hurt someone or wound up hurting themselves."

Kendal stepped forward and wrapped her arms around my neck. "Well, I'm not going to let her hurt you. She might as well give up and stop coming around because there is nothing she can say or do that will change a thing."

"I concur with that statement." I pecked Kendal's lips and pulled my head back to look at her. "So, what did you think when you saw her? Did you know who she was or did it take a while?"

"It took a minute, but her voice still sounds the same. Parts of her face looked the same too, but I'm not gon' lie and say I wasn't spooked out by her new look. She actually looked kind of dope. What you think?"

"She looks nice. But it's funny that I, not one time, picked up on anything that reminded me of the old her. Not even when I had sex—"

I paused right when the word "sex" left my mouth. Kendal cocked her head back and narrowed her eyes as she looked at me.

"You had sex with her? When?"

"It was by accident."

"Accident? Like how do you have sex with somebody by accident? You told me she was trying to chase you and trick you so she could set you up again. Not once did you mention that you had sex with her. That shit is disgusting."

She walked away from me. When I reached for her hand, she snatched it away. I definitely wasn't in the mood for her bullshit tonight. If it wasn't for *her* fucking mother, none of this would be happening.

"Don't you snatch away from me when I'm talking to you." I followed her to the bedroom. She lit a blunt and sat on the edge of the bed.

"What in the hell do you want me to say, Brent? Should I be happy right now, knowing that you had sex with her?"

"I'm not saying that, but what you not gon' do is disrespect me. Put that damn blunt down, come back into the kitchen and continue to talk to me like you got some sense."

Kendal ignored me. She blew smoke into the air and winced while giving me a hard stare. I didn't have time for her shit. She always tried me at the wrong time. That's what infuriated me about her, and I wasn't having it today.

"Don't make me repeat myself again. I'm going to the kitchen. You got two minutes to make your move and meet me there. Two, Kendal, and not a minute longer."

I went back into the kitchen and stood. Two minutes had come and gone. Kendal knew I was coming for her, but when I did, I halted my steps right at the door. She remained on the bed with a blunt tightened between her lips and a gun in her hand. Her eyes were still narrowed as she looked at me.

"Even though I pretend that I don't have a problem with all these other tricks you be screwing," she said, after removing the blunt. "You need to know that I do. When it comes to my mother, you need not to go there ever again. I need to know that you are one hundred percent clear about what I just said to you."

"Your words are still a little fuzzy to me. And if I'm not clear, what are you going to do? Shoot me?"

I strolled into the room and stood in front of her. As she looked up at me, I took her hand with the gun and positioned it against my chest. I then smacked the blunt from her other hand and stomped it with my foot.

"Fool, you really think I won't shoot you, don't you?" she said.

"I'm one hundred and ten percent sure that you won't, but if you're brave enough to ever pull that motherfucker out on me again, I suggest you be brave enough to use it."

Kendal let the gun swing on her finger then dropped it. When it fell to the ground, I kicked it away from me.

"Good thing it wasn't loaded," she teased.

"Yeah, and it's a good thing that my belt still gon' sting that ass when I hit you with it."

I removed my belt, and as Kendal tried to back away from me on the bed, I grabbed her ankle and pulled her towards me. She kicked her legs, but calmed down when I struck her leg one good time. After that, I tossed the belt on the floor and lay on top of her.

"That shit hurt!" she yelled. "I told you to stop doing that. That's not how you do somebody you claim to love."

I wrapped her legs around my back and rubbed the swollen red welt on her leg. My lips touched hers; our foreheads were pressed together. "But I do love you. If I didn't, I wouldn't have done all of this for you. I would've walked a long time ago, but I didn't. I stayed because I knew how much you needed me. I wanted to be there for you, and that's what I never, ever want you to forget."

I tried to kiss Kendal, but she turned her head to the side. She was being real difficult today, but I understood why. Seeing her mother bothered her. It probably made her feel that all of this was in some way wrong. I had to assure her that it wasn't.

"I love you, too, but please don't hurt me, Brent. I don't know what I would do without—"

"Look at me," I whispered. "Close your mouth and look at me right now."

She turned her head. I searched into her beautiful, big round eyes and fed her my bullshit. "You will never lose me, and I'm not going to hurt you. Why? Because we've come a long way together. I've been with you longer than anyone—you can trust me. I need you to trust me and know that I'm doing everything that I can for us. Don't let your mother break us. She can't break us, and you have to promise me you won't let that happen."

"I promise," she softly said. She gave me a sweet kiss, and I moved down low to prove to her how much I appreciated her unwavering commitment to me. I was convinced that Kendal wasn't going anywhere. She wasn't going to ever betray me and neither would any of the others. Why? Because I was, and have always been, one charming motherfucker. Then again, I guess that depended on who you asked.

CHAPTER EIGHTEEN

I hadn't gotten any sleep at all. I tried, but there was too much on my mind. I felt lost. Felt like I was going crazy and I seriously wanted to hurt someone. There was nothing positive about this situation. Everything Kendal said to me that day kept playing over and over again in my head. I felt responsible for all of this, and even though Brent had done quite a number on me and my child, I still felt like I shouldn't have allowed things to go as far as they did.

Maybe if I had been paying a little more attention to how Brent looked at her, how he always wanted her to be a part of what we did, and how he kept trying to do nice things for her, maybe I would have picked up on something. I hated myself for this. I swear I did, but what could I really do to fix it? I didn't know, but taunting Brent and Eric gave me some satisfaction. As I lay across the bed, waiting for Eric to take the call, I tossed back the bottle of Hennessy and thought about what I'd done less than a few hours ago. It was terrible. Really bad, but it felt good to watch all the damage from a distance.

"Officer Eric Wayne speaking," he said.

"Say muthafuckaaaa," I slurred then chugged down more alcohol. I wiped across my mouth and cleared my throat. "Listen up, okay? If you ain't already hurrrrd, I did something that's gon' really make you mad. But before I tell you what I did, I want to remind you to do your job biiiiotch. Do your job and go talk to those girls! All of them. Every last one of them and check that nigga out! As for the other little thingy." I laughed and sipped more of the Henny. "Well, you know that little cabin of yours in Lake of the Ozarks, where you take your main lady and some of your tricks? Well, the roof, the roof, the roof is on fiyaaah! It will need some water so it does not fuckin' burn!" I got up and danced around the room while singing. "Burn muthafucka, burn!"

"Abby, enjoy your freedom while it lasts."

He hung up on me. I fell back on the bed, laughing. Laughed so hard so I wouldn't cry. When I heard the door open, I jumped up from the bed and ran out of the room to see who it was. Jeff stood at the door with a grocery bag in his hand. He closed his eyes because all I had on was a thong and some socks.

"Girrrrl, will you please go put on some clothes! You gon' make a gay man like me turn straight in this muthafucka and tear yo ass up. Stop being so damn nasty!"

I laughed and went back to the bedroom to put on a robe. When I came back, Jeff was already putting some of the groceries he'd bought in the fridge.

"Since you were sounding so out of it yesterday, I thought I'd stop by and cook you something. I know yo bony self ain't been eating nothing, but wait until you taste my lasagna."

I sat at the stool in front of the counter, watching Jeff put on an apron to prepare the food.

"I'm not really hungry. I'm sure your lasagna is delicious, but I'm not in the mood to eat anything."

"I don't care if you're in the mood or not. If you're in the mood to drink, you can get in the mood to eat."

"Whatever. I just don't want you to waste your time."

"No, you're the one wasting your time with Brent and with your daughter. After you told me what she did, girrrrrl, I would've beat her ass!" Jeff slammed his fist on the counter. "That shit made me mad! I thought about it all night. It took everything for me not to go over there and wear her ass out!"

"I know. Trust me, I know how you feel, but she's my daughter, Jeff. I just couldn't do what I really wanted to do."

"Daughter or no daughter, she would be dead. Ain't nobody got time for that messiness, and she should know better. Be tricked by the dick all you want, but disrespecting yo Mama, the woman who gave birth to you, that's a whole nother story. She shouldn't even be alive today."

"Jeff, stop. You don't know how I feel because you didn't give birth to her. You don't know what it feels like to birth a child and love them so much like I do. As much as I want to, I can't turn my back on her. She doesn't realize it yet, but she's going to need me. When she does, I want to be there for her."

Jeff rubbed my hand real hard. He wet his hand with water and rubbed my hand again.

"What are you doing?" I said, laughing.

"I'm trying to see if that blackness on your hand will wash off. You got to be white underneath there, because that's some white mama bullshit you just said to me. That girl called you a stank bitch, told you to go fuck yourself, reminded you that she screwed your man and dared you to do anything about it. Now, if that ain't affiliated with the devil, I don't quite know what is. Mama or no mama, a real black mama knows when to wash her hands and turn that bitch loose."

"Okay, Jeff. Now, what you ain't gon' do is call my daughter out of her name. Chill out and let's not talk about this anymore because I'm getting upset."

"Fine. I'm not gon' say another word, except for this. You were wrong on so many different levels, but you didn't deserve to be treated that way. Everybody has to take responsibility for their own actions, and Kendal ain't got no room to be calling you out like that when she done succumbed to the puppet master."

"Fine, Jeff. But is it really her fault, though? Can I blame her for this? I don't think that's fair. It's not and I don't care what you say."

"Look. If Obama can be blamed for everything that has gone wrong in this damn country, and #45 is president, then surely I can figure out a way to blame your trifling dau—" Jeff paused, after seeing the look on my face. "Okay, like I said, I'm done."

"Thank you. Now, pour me some wine and let's talk about something else."

Jeff poured both of us a glass of wine and raised his glass so we could toast. "Let's toast to you getting some good dick soon. You are stressed the hell out, and I hope you find something that'll relax you."

"Well, it won't be that because I am done with men. I don't think I will ever date again. Just thinking about it frustrates me."

He pursed his lips and nodded. "If you say so, sure. I believe you."

He laughed and sipped from the glass of wine. So did I. I was so serious about never dating again. Brent had changed the game for sure. Trusting anyone wasn't going to happen, and to be frank, being with a man wasn't even on my mind.

Jeff and I ate dinner and parlayed in the living room, watching TV. My belly was full. The lasagna was off the chain. It was the best I'd ever had and I thanked Jeff over and over again.

"I told you I could throw down. Next time, I'mma make you a pot roast. Girl, that stuff will make you wanna slap yo Mama like Kendal did you and get away with it."

I shot Jeff an evil glare.

"Okay, I quit. I'mma leave you alone and finish watching this movie. After that, I'mma take my butt home and get some rest."

I told Jeff to be quiet and watch the movie. By the time it was over, he was crashed out on the sofa. I was tired, but like always, I couldn't sleep. I sat in bed, tapping my cellphone against my hand. I knew Eric could find me by checking my cellphone. But why hadn't he done it yet? I'd called him from this very room. I expected him to bust the door down and arrest me. It wasn't that difficult to find me, was it? Maybe, just maybe, he knew something that I didn't. I held the phone in my hand and sent Brent a text message.

WHY ASSHOLE WHY? WHY COULDN'T YOU JUST LEAVE ME AND MY DAUGHTER ALONE?

Less than five minutes later, he responded.

I DON'T KNOW WHAT YOU'RE TALKING ABOUT. LEAVE ME ALONE.

YES YOU DO. YOU KNOW DAMN WELL WHAT I'M TALKING ABOUT. YOU SHOULD BE AFRAID. VERY AFRAID BECAUSE I'M COMING FOR YOU AGAIN.

LOOKING FORWARD TO SEEING YOU SOON BITCH.

I dropped the phone on the bed, reminding myself to tell Jeff I needed another gun.

CHAPTER NINETEEN

OFFICER ERIC WAYNE

Abby had lost her mind. I called the resort in Lake of the Ozarks to check on the property I'd purchased three years ago. It was almost a two hour drive away from where I lived, so I didn't have time to go there myself. Either way, the young man who answered the phone told me there had been a fire. He said it happened by accident and I needed to get there as soon as I could. When I got there that day, my cabin was almost burned to the ground. For insurance purposes, I told no one how it actually happened. I kept it to myself, and was furious about all these games Abby was playing. I'd finally spoken with some other officers about what she'd been up to. We put a plan in motion to find and arrest her. She had gotten ruthless; it was time for her to be stopped.

Right before baseball practice started, I told Brent what Abby had done.

"You're right. This has to stop," he said. "And if you don't put a stop to this, I promise you I will. She's been texting me, threatening me, still harassing me and everything. How long are we going to let this go on?"

"I already told you I have everything under control. Her day is coming. I'm trying to play my cards right because I don't want any slipups this time. Once she's behind bars, she needs to stay there. I don't ever want to have to deal with her shit again."

"Same here."

Practice started and we had a great time. All the fun and jokes helped take my mind off everything, and the fellas and me were ready to take on our first team. The game wasn't until next week, and right after practice was over, one of the other officers, Trenton, asked if we all wanted to meet at Sybergs Bar & Grill to get some wings and drinks. I was all for it. So was everybody else, including Brent who stressed how much he needed to get his mind off things. When we arrived at Sybergs, the waitress seated us at several tables upfront, right where a live band was playing. They brought the house down, and everybody was singing along to the music and dancing. While I was talking to an officer about an upcoming murder case next week, I saw Brent looking frustrated while speaking to someone over the phone. His hand gestures implied that he wasn't too happy. He kept moving the phone away from his ear, sighing. I wondered if the caller was Abby bugging him. He pushed the doors open to go outside, and that's when I got up. I didn't want him to see me, so I exited from another door and moved along the side of the building. I saw a car pull up, and when Brent got inside, the person driving parked on the parking lot. Unable to see who the driver was, I eased across the parking lot, getting as close as I could to the vehicle without being seen. That's when I saw a young lady behind the steering wheel. She looked familiar, but I wasn't exactly sure where I'd seen her before. She and Brent appeared to be arguing. Her mouth was going a mile a minute; I could tell she was upset about something. He kept staring ahead, taking deep breaths and turning his head to look out the window. That's when she pushed his head and made it hit the window. After that, all I saw was his fist in the air, pounding her with blow after blow. She had crouched down in her seat, trying to block his punches. I was unable to stand there and watch this go on. I rushed up to the car and pulled on the passenger's side door handle. My presence didn't stop Brent. He kept on punching her; I had to drag him out of the car.

"Fucking bitch," he yelled. "I told you about putting your gotdamn hands on me, didn't I, Toya?"

I struggled to get him a few feet away from the car, and when I did, he looked like a madman. Sweat ran down his face and his fists were still tightened. I held him from behind, trying my best to calm him down.

"Man, what in the hell are you doing?" I barked. "Don't you dare hit no woman like that."

"He's a punk," the young lady spewed while inside of the car. Blood dripped from her nose and her lip was busted wide open. "A fucking punk. I hate yo fucking ass! I swear to God this time I am done with you."

Brent struggled to get loose from my grip; he tried to go after her again. I released him and pushed him further away from the car. "Stop, alright. Go back inside and chill the fuck out. You don't need to do this, man. You're better than this and she is not worth it!"

He straightened his shirt and kept mean mugging the chick in the car. Once he was calm, he went back inside. I tried to catch the young lady before she drove off the parking lot. But when she saw me coming towards her, the car sped away. To say I was shocked would be an understatement. What in the hell was going on with Brent? He and I needed to talk. I didn't want to wait until later, so I went inside and asked him to meet me on the outdoor patio where there was only two couples dining.

"I know what you're thinking," Brent said, pacing back and forth with his hands dipped in his pockets.

"You have no idea what I'm thinking. No matter what I'm thinking, I will say this. You had no right, whatsoever, to put your hands on her like that."

"Like hell I didn't. She punched and slapped the shit out of me. Knocked my head into the window and kept spitting on me while she call herself talking to me. I don't know what your parents taught you, but mine taught me that when people are brave enough to hit you, hit those muthafuckas back."

I was so upset with him that I got in his face. "And I'm here to tell you that your gotdamn parents were wrong! There is never any reason to put your hands on a woman like that. Not even a full grown woman, but a young fucking girl! You should've been man enough to get out of the car and walk the hell away from her. Those damn licks didn't hurt you. Maybe your pride, nigga, but that's about it. Get over it and man the fuck up!"

Brent was so mad that he tried to walk away. I placed my hand on his chest to stop him. "Nah, bro, I'm not done yet. If I ever see you do any shit like that again, I'm going to arrest you. Arrest you and throw you under the jail for putting me in this predicament and for having your damn back when I shouldn't have. Got it?"

He removed my hand from his chest and tossed his head back. I was too upset to go back inside, and instead of going home for the night, I went to the police station. I remembered Brent calling the young lady Toya, and when I checked my text messages, Toya Ferguson was the name Abby had sent me, along with her address. I searched her name in the database, finding out as much information about her as I could. She went to Hazelwood High and was eighteen years old. Had been arrested before for shoplifting and she also had a resisting arrest charge on her police record. After what had happened tonight, I was eager to go talk to her in the morning.

A little after nine in the morning, I drove to Toya's house. The car I'd seen yesterday was in the driveway. A small poodle was on the porch, the bushes needed to be trimmed, grass was too high and the window on the front door was cracked. I went to the door and rang the doorbell. I heard someone walk to the door, but they never said anything. I figured my police vehicle in the driveway made Toya scared.

"Helloooo," I said through the door.

A few seconds later, she replied. "What?"

"Toya," I said, politely. "Is that you?"

"Yes. But who wants to know?"

"I'm Officer Wayne. I was at the restaurant last night when you and Brent started fighting."

"And?"

"I would like to speak to you about it, if you don't mind."

"I do mind. I don't have nothing else to say about it, so please leave me alone."

"I wish I could do that, but I can't. Please open the door so we can talk, okay?"

There was a long pause, before I heard her remove the chain from the door. When she opened the door, she barely cracked it. She cracked it enough, though, for me to see her face. I guess she was embarrassed by the bruises.

"Now what?" she said. "Am I being arrested for something?"

"No, not at all. I would like to come inside, if you don't mind. Are you alone or is your mother here with you? If she is, I would like to speak to her, too."

"She's out of town. I'm not supposed to let nobody in here, and what makes you think I trust you. You're the police. I don't get down with the police like that."

"I understand how you feel, but you can trust me. The majority of us do care about people, and if I didn't care, I wouldn't even be here."

She was quiet. A few minutes later, she opened the door and invited me to come inside. Trying to hide her face, she kept her head lowered while sitting in a chair. She told me to sit in another one. I removed my cap and sat less than six or seven feet away from her. She had no idea how horrible I felt about this situation. I feared hearing the truth, and was upset with myself for possibly waiting this long to hear it.

"Tell me about your relationship with Brent," I said.

"There's really not much to say about it. Just like any other relationship, we have our ups and downs. Sometimes it's good; sometimes it's bad. What else do you want me to say?"

"I want you to tell me about the bad times. What makes it bad? When he hits you?"

She shrugged and kept her head lowered. "I guess. We just argue a lot. It's always over stupid shit. Things get blown out of proportion like they did last night. Looking back on it, I was wrong for putting my hands on him. I have a bad temper and I need to learn how to control it."

"Maybe so, but you do know that it's not right for a man to put his hands on you like that, don't you?"

"I know."

"Good. And it's okay to tell someone if he does. Would you like to press charges?"

"No."

"Why not?"

"Because I don't want to. Besides, we'll work it out."

"That's what a lot of women say, Toya, and then it's too late. You don't ever want to find yourself in a situation where it's too late for you to do anything. I know how much you care about Brent, but what about you? You deserve better than this, don't you?"

She wiped a tear that rolled down her cheek. "Yes."

"Then, press charges against him. I'll go arrest him right now, if you decide to press charges against him."

She moved her head from side-to-side. Seeing how difficult this was for her, I got up and kneeled in front of her. I wanted her to know there were police officers who cared. There were men who didn't like this kind of shit and didn't approve of it. I lifted her chin and made her look at me.

"What are you afraid of?" I asked. "I got your back, but I want you to tell me why are you so afraid?"

More tears fell from her eyes. "I'm afraid of losing him. I don't want to lose him. He's all I got. You don't understand that he's all I have."

Her words tore me up. It took a lot to bring me to tears; I blinked to clear my eyes. I reached out to comfort her, and as I held her trembling body, she was so concerned about Brent.

"He's not going to go to jail, is he?" she asked. "I don't want him to get locked up."

I backed away from her and couldn't make her any promises. "I don't know what's going to happen to Brent, but I don't want you to worry about him. I want you to take care of yourself. How old are you now?"

I already knew, but I wanted to see how old she was when she started having sex with Brent.

"I'm eighteen."

"How old were you when you and Brent started having sex?"

"I had just turned seventeen. And just so you know, I pursued him. He didn't pursue me. I was the one who wanted him."

I stood and gave her some tissue so she could wipe her eyes and nose. "Maybe you didn't know better, Toya, but he very well should have. Thanks for talking to me. If you ever need anything, just pick up the phone and call me at the station."

I gave her my card. She stood to walk me to the door. "Thank you," she said. "I didn't think police were nice, but you pretty cool."

"I told you I was, didn't I?"

She smiled and that made me smile. After I left, I was on my way back to Hazelwood High to see Brent again. While I was en route, I got a text message that made me pull over.

IT'S ABOUT TIME YOU DID WHAT THE FUCK I TOLD YOU TO DO. NOW WHAT ASSHOLE?

I replied: FUCK YOU

I looked around, but all I saw were cars passing me by. Abby was on some wild shit that was driving me insane. I hated she was leading me down a path I didn't want to go. How hard would it be for me to admit I had been wrong?

CHAPTER TWENTY

BRENT CARSON

I had to admit that Eric showing up as often as he had was starting to worry me. This time, however, he was there to give me an ultimatum. I didn't like it one bit.

"Resign. You need to resign today or else I'm going to do something you're not going to like."

"E, I can't believe you're here talking all this bullshit. All because you saw me fighting with a young lady who had just attacked me and called me names. I'm confused. Am I not allowed to defend myself? Please tell me what does any of this have to do with me working here?"

"Brent, stop with the games. I can't protect you anymore, and I don't like this path I'm about to travel down with you. I spoke to Toya earlier. Before you get all upset with her, she didn't tell me anything I didn't already know. She was trying her best to protect you, and I'm so pissed at you for taking advantage of her. Her, April and only God knows who else. You can't lie to me anymore. You are so lucky that these young ladies were seventeen when you started fucking around with them. Missouri law is fucked up and I hate that shit. But I know for a fact that schools prohibit teachers from being involved in any way with students. That's why you need to resign. Right now, before you find yourself in a messy ass, embarrassing situation you can't get out of."

His words silenced me for a while. I wasn't sure what to say, and I didn't want to incriminate myself in any way. I knew damn well what the laws were in Missouri, but I slipped when it came to Kendal. She, however, would never tell anyone. Abby could say whatever she wanted, but who in the hell would believe her? Either way, I felt heat swinging my way. I couldn't get around this thing with Toya and April. Eric knew too much, so I had to do what he asked of me.

"I don't like this, but you're right. The administrators here would have a big problem with my relationships, but I want you to know a few things, before you walk out that door. All I wanted to do was be there for these young ladies. They were lost, and every time they came into my office to converse with me, I gave them hope. I made them feel better about themselves, and after a while, they did. I do regret getting involved with them sexually and I admit to crossing the line. That's why I'm prepared to leave here. I'm going to leave them alone, so you don't have to worry about me putting my hands on nobody again."

Eric strolled up to my desk and looked me dead in my eyes. "You weren't there for them. You were only there for yourself. You used them and took advantage of them. Don't you dare try to feed me your bullshit lies. I'm not the one easily convinced. If I had enough evidence to arrest you, I would. So be careful, Brent. Be real careful and think long and hard about how you move forward. I'll be watching you, and if I just so happen to get a little busy, you need to know that someone else is watching you, too."

He pivoted and left my office. I took a deep breath, leaned back in my chair and pondered. I guess it was them against me now. That was unfortunate because the one thing I was never classified as was a loser. I had to make sure everybody still had my back and wouldn't turn on me. Right after I typed up my resignation letter, I made my way to Toya's house to see her. After that, Kendal and I needed to have a long talk.

I called Toya, telling her I was on my way. She was already outside waiting for me, and when I pulled in the driveway, she came to my car. A cap was on her head; she kept it down so I wouldn't see her face. When she got in the car, she removed the cap and faced me. I could now see all the damage I had done. It wasn't pretty and I felt bad about the shit. I knew I'd had a bad temper. Always had, always would. It had gotten worse, after

Lajuanna left me. That's why it was hard for me to be with women who provoked me. As long as the woman I was with was nice and stayed in her place, shit like this would never happen. Not once did I put my hands on Lajuanna. We'd gotten into heated arguments, but she didn't hit me and I didn't hit her. The same went for Abby—back in the day. As much shit as she'd done to me, I never went there. Had I known Viola was her at the time, I would've done more because she deserved it.

"Where are you taking me?" Toya asked. "I'm not in the mood to have sex, so don't take me to your place."

"Where do you want to go then? Would you like to take a trip, go on vacation . . . go to the moon? Anywhere you want to go, just tell me."

"And then what, Brent? You bring me back here and the same shit keep happening over and over again? This shit is crazy. I don't want to do this with you anymore, and I really do mean it this time."

I reached for her hand, but when I touched it she jerked back. I touched it again, and brought it up to my lips. After I planted a delicate kiss on her hand, I laid it on my lap. "I'm sorry for putting my hands on you, and don't sit there and act like this happens all the time. You be pushing me, Toya. Treating me like shit and talking to me like I'm one of these lil' dumb niggas you done met on Instagram or Snapchat. Whether we continue to see each other or not is your choice. It has always been your choice and I'll rock with anything you decide. I just want you to be happy. I resigned today, and since I'm going to have a little time on my hand, I thought you might want to take a vacation somewhere. Just you and me. What do you think about that?"

She seemed to be in deep thought as she stared ahead while touching her lips. "Why did you resign?"

"Because Officer Wayne came to my job and told me to. I know he came over here to see you—"

She rushed to speak up. "But I didn't say anything to him that—"

"I know, baby. Trust me, I know. But my job prohibits me from being involved with students. I crossed the line and now I'm out of a job."

"I'm sorry to hear that. What you gon' do now?"

"Hopefully, spend more time with you. Maybe we can put more effort into trying to get this right. That's if you want to. If you don't, I understand."

"I do. I really do, Brent, but not right now. I need to back away from this for a while. It's too much for me to handle, and I got other things I need to be focused on. I hope you get that."

Her words let me know I was slipping. I had to be real careful, because Toya would turn on me in a second. I wasn't sure what Eric said to her earlier. Obviously, something he'd said must have gotten through to her.

"I do get that. I want you to focus on those things and be all that you can be. If I'm a distraction, cool, let me go. Just know that I'm here for you, I will always be here for you, if you need me."

"That's good to know. I'll be here for you, too."

"In what way, Toya?"

"In giving you whatever you need. Not what you want, but what you need."

I wasn't sure what she meant, so I took it a step further. "I don't want much, but what I need is for you to stop talking to people about us. It's not a good look for either of us, especially for me because I'm the one who is going to catch heat for being in a relationship with you. Many people don't like it. They think it's wrong, but they don't understand the bond we share. I know you get it, don't you?"

She removed her hand from my lap and lifted her head to look at me. "Yes, I get it. I get all of it and you don't have to worry about me saying anything to anyone else. I'm not going to say another word. Let's just be done with this and please stop reaching out to me. It's hard saying no to you, but whenever I don't hear from you I do just fine."

This was her way of breaking me down gently. I thought it was kind of cute. As long as she agreed to stop talking to people about us, I was good with that. I reached out with my finger and rubbed the side of her face.

"You know I love you, don't you?" I said.

She didn't respond.

"Maybe one day you'll realize how much. Goodbye, Toya."

I leaned in to kiss her cheek, but she moved her head away from me. She reached for the door handle, slightly opening the door.

"Bye Brent," she said. "I love you too."

I was encouraged by her words and released a deep breath. It appeared that I was covered, but I could never be so sure. I waited until Toya was in the house, before I drove away. I felt kind of saddened by the way things ended between us, and as I was in deep thought, Karla's name and number flashed on my phone. I thought she was calling to tell me Eric had been in touch with her. Instead, she called to inquire about the monthly payments for the five grand I'd borrowed.

"Damn, baby, it ain't even the fifteenth of the month yet. Why are you bugging me already?"

"I'm just calling to remind you," she snapped. She wasn't snapping when I was fucking her, so this was quite surprising to me.

"I don't need any reminders. I'll do what I can to make the payment, but as a heads up, I'm no longer employed. There is a possibility that you and your husband might have to make the initial payment."

At that point, she lost it. I had never heard her cuss before, and as a woman of God, so she said, this didn't shock me one bit.

"Don't start playing games with me motherfucker! You said you would pay it—"

I hit the end button on my phone. Too much messy shit was piling up. Karla had to wait until some of it died down. When she called back, I didn't answer my phone. She then sent a text message, but when I read it, I saw that it wasn't from her. It was from Abby.

LOOKS LIKE YOUR WORLD IS ABOUT TO CRUMBLE. DON'T FORGET I'M COMING FOR YOU.

At first, I didn't respond to her. But I knew how to get underneath her skin. I parked my car in Kendal's apartment complex, and then replied to Abby's text.

LOOKS LIKE YOUR FACE IS ABOUT TO CRACK. I'M ABOUT TO CUM TOO. ALL UP IN YOUR DAUGHTER. SHE IS SO MUCH BETTER THAN YOU EVER WERE AND HER HEAD GAME IS SICK!

I figured that would quiet her for a while. She didn't reply, so I went inside to have a talk with Kendal.

"You wouldn't lie to me, would you?" I asked while sitting on the bed. I kept puffing on a cigar; my nerves were a little shaky.

"No, I wouldn't lie to you, especially not about the police coming here asking questions. They'd better not come here. I don't snitch, nor do I kiss and then turn around and tell."

Kendal was rock solid. That's why she was my fav. I would do anything for her. It was too damn bad that her mother was Abby. On her hands and knees, Kendal crawled over to where I was.

"So, what are you going to do about your job?" she asked.

"Not sure yet. Maybe I'll stop working altogether and put you to work."

"Hmmm, I don't like the sound of that, especially since I know what kind of work you might be talking about."

I removed the cigar and looked at all this beautifulness in front of me. Kendal definitely had the skills, and the mindset, to set us up good and put us in position to never want for anything.

"Letting another man touch, kiss and feel you like I do would drive me nuts. That will never happen, and you need to recognize when I'm just playing with you."

She crawled forward to give me a kiss. As we indulged, I kept thinking to myself that if push came to shove, anything was possible.

CHAPTER TWENTY-ONE

I'd been driving Brent and Eric crazy with my text messages. But the one Brent sent shook me. I had to cool out for a while, and I took Jeff's advice to pamper myself, just for one day. One day without sending text messages to Brent or Eric and not following them around. I couldn't help myself, but I had to know everything they'd been up to.

It felt good to finally see Eric making some moves. I wasn't sure what prompted him to do it, and I figured he had something to do with Brent no longer working. Maybe Toya decided to speak up and share what she knew about Brent. I'd thought that an adult having sex with a seventeen-year-old was considered a crime in Missouri, but I was wrong. It was under seventeen, and if the adult was under twenty, it wasn't considered a crime at all. Whoever came up with that law needed to be shot. It was wrong for so many different reasons, and even though Toya might have been seventeen when she started having sex with Brent, Kendal wasn't. She was younger than that. I knew it, he knew it and she knew it, too. Nonetheless, I just couldn't get through to her. Not yet, anyway. I wasn't giving up, because her coming forth was key to getting Brent put behind bars for a long time.

After I left Jeff's beauty salon, I went to Bar Louie's in the Central West End. I needed to get a bite to eat, toss back a few drinks and just chill. The second I entered, I saw Drew sitting at the bar. My mind traveled to the day he'd given me the hundred bucks and Sade. I wondered what she'd been up to and if her uncle had made any moves yet. Maybe Drew could give me an update. I wasn't sure if he'd be willing to tell me how he was involved in my escape plan, but I wanted to fill him out and see what was up.

I made my way over to him in a pair of slim-fitting jeans, a silk, money-green shirt that had a wrap around the neck and yellow snake-skin heels. Jeff had me looking real stylish these days, and with my hair trimmed, lined and slicked on my head, I felt pretty good.

"Is anyone sitting here," I asked as I stood next to the stool by Drew.

He looked me up and down, before replying, "No."

I took a seat and immediately flagged the bartender to get something to drink. "I'll have a glass of Moscato."

The bartender put a coaster in front of me and walked away. As Drew watched the baseball game on TV, I attempted to get his attention. I cleared my throat and started talking to myself out loud.

"Shoot, no I didn't. How did I forget to do that?"

He turned his head to look at me. Just like the first time I saw him, his long locs were mostly on one side. The other side of his hair was almost shaved off but sharply lined. Casually dressed, he wore jeans and a black V-neck tee. A gold necklace dangled from his neck and there was a sexy mole on the lower right side of his cheek. I hadn't paid much attention to it before, but being this close to him, I was able to observe so much more.

"Did you say something to me?" he asked.

"No, I was just talking to myself. I forgot to let my dog out, before I left the house. He's probably so pissed at me right now. I know he's going to do something revengeful to make me pay for it."

He chuckled and took a sip of the dark liquid he was drinking. "Maybe so, but dogs are forgiving. Loyalty, too, so don't forget that."

He turned his head to watch the game again. I guess my conversation about dogs wasn't enough to keep him tuned in, so I quickly changed the subject.

"Who are the Cardinals playing?" I asked, referring to the game. "Are they playing at the Busch Stadium today?"

"Nah, not today. They're playing the Milwaukee Brewers."

"I'm not that into sports, but I hope they're winning."

Drew looked at the TV, glanced at me again, smirked and then took another sip of his drink. "Yeah, they're winning, but tell me something, okay?"

"What's that?"

"Is this how women approach brothers these days? I mean, I haven't been approached in quite some time, so I'm not sure about how it works anymore."

He blushed—his dimples were so cute. "If I were you, I wouldn't exactly flatter myself. What would make you think I'm trying to come on to you?"

He held his hands up. "My bad. Maybe I'm wrong, but are you? Be honest."

I shrugged and smiled. "Maybe. Maybe I am. Now what?"

"Well, if you're interested, why don't I give you my number and you can hit me up later. My friends will be here shortly and I'm going to be occupied chit-chatting with them."

"Gotcha. How about if you're interested, why don't you give me a call later? Here's my number. Lock it into your phone, in case you lose the napkin."

I wrote my number on the napkin and got up to walk away. He looked at the napkin and then at me. "So, you're not going to tell me your name?"

"Oops, I almost forgot. It's, uh, Abby. Abigail Wilson, but my friends call me Abby."

I walked away, but by the time I got to the door to exit, I heard Drew call after me.

"Wait," he said, following me out the door and down the street. "Did you say your name was Abigail Wilson?"

"I sure did. Why are you asking?"

"Be . . . because I know someone by that name."

I stopped walking and faced him. "How well do you know her?"

He scratched his head and folded his arms. "Not well. Look, I'm sorry. I'm tripping. I was just thinking about something. When you said that name, it threw me off a bit."

I was going to mess with Drew a while longer, but I decided to let him off the hook. "No need to apologize. I know you don't recognize me, as I do look quite different."

Drew's brows shot up. He gazed at me with a puzzled expression on his face. "Really?" he said. "Abby? Stop playing."

I held out my arms and turned around. "In the flesh. Your hundred bucks didn't do all of this, but it most certainly helped."

"Daaaaaamn," he said, checking me out. He chuckled while covering his mouth. "I can't believe this. You done hooked yourself up. You were pretty before, but I do like the new look as well."

"Thanks for the compliment. I'm glad we have a chance to talk and I do want to know so much more. But first, how's my girl? Have you heard anything from her?"

Drew's demeanor quickly changed. His smile vanished. From the way he looked at me, I knew his response wasn't going to be good.

"I guess you don't know, huh? About three weeks ago, Sade was found dead in her cell. They say it was suicide. I'm not sure what happened, but I don't believe she would've killed herself. She had hopes and dreams. I know, because we talked a lot. She wanted to get out of that place, and there was a chance of that happening. Her uncle was starting to shake things up. Maybe some people didn't like it. Either way, she's gone."

The news about Sade just broke my heart. It just never worked out for women like us, did it? I was crushed. And as I became emotional, Drew reached out to hold me.

"Just so you know, she thought you was really good people," he said. "That's why she wanted to help you. She told me everything and encouraged me to help you. When they needed a security detail to escort you to the hospital that day, I stepped up. I volunteered, and all along I knew you were trying to be free."

I backed away from him, wiping my tears. "Thank you so much. I did what I could to help Sade, but I guess it wasn't enough. She was so sweet. I never would've made it without her being there. I just hate that it had to end like this."

"Yeah, me too. While I didn't get in trouble for what had happened that day with you, I did quit after I found out what happened to Sade. People running those jails are wicked. I guess I don't have to tell you that. You probably already know."

Of course I knew. They were terrible and black people in there, especially, didn't have a chance. Drew told me he needed to get back inside to hook up with his friends. He also asked if it would be okay for him to call me later. While I really wasn't feeling up to it, I still told him to call me. I went home and did what I knew best. Got drunk so I could wash away some of this pain. I wanted to send Brent a text message, but the last thing I needed was for him to say something to me about Kendal. I did, however, send a text to Eric. I wasn't surprised that he responded, because he often did.

ARE YOU MAKING ANY PROGRESS?

NONE OF YOUR BUSINESS, BUT STOP ALL THIS TEXTING AND COME SEE ME SO WE CAN TALK AGAIN.

YOU MUST BE OUT OF YOUR MIND. ALL YOU WANT TO DO IS ARREST ME.

TRUE, BUT STILL COME SEE ME.

FUCK YOU. NOT A CHANCE IN HELL.

THINK ABOUT IT. IT'S TIME.

I tossed the phone on the bed, and while lying sideways, a pillow was tucked between my legs. I was so tired of feeling sorry for myself, but I felt helpless. Reality was starting to kick in, and I was starting to think there was nothing I could do to help Kendal. Maybe she had to weather her storm alone, just like many people did who found themselves in similar situations. It seemed like Eric was doing something. Then again, it could've been a trick to get me to come to the police station so he could arrest me. At this point, I just didn't know what else to do. Texting and following them around didn't seem like enough.

My cellphone vibrated; I figured it was Drew.

"Are you busy?" he asked.

"I'm just lying down. Can't sleep, but I'm here."

"Is it okay for me to come over? I understand if you don't want to be bothered right now. I just thought you might want some company."

"Drew, stop trying to be nice. Most men aren't nice and you all want something. But you know what? So do I. Come over and take care of me so I can finally get some rest."

"Shoot me your address, and I'll be on my way."

"The door will be unlocked. You can find me in the bedroom."

Less than an hour later, Drew found me in the bedroom. I was very tipsy and ready for whatever he was willing to give. He stood next to the bed, removing his clothes. Talk about super sexy, he definitely was. My mouth watered at the sight of his sculptured, chocolicious body. He smelled good, too, and when he lay on top of me, I inhaled his masculine scent. Our eyes stayed connected; lips were locked tight. His felt soft like butter and he kept delicately sucking my lips with his. That let me know how well he performed orally. I was so ready for him to taste me, and in a matter of minutes, he went there. The length of his tongue reached the depths of my soul. I squirmed around like a slithering snake and gripped the sheets as he worked wonders. I needed this so badly, and in the midst of it all, I tried not to think about everything I had been going through. I kept my eyes closed and shook my head from side-to-side to wash away my thoughts. Drew held my hips down, while trying to calm my whimpers with each delicate lick. When the time came for us to step it up a bit, he rolled me on top and directed me to ride him. I was ready. I thought I was ready, but shit went south real quick. I felt nothing as he entered me. His strokes weren't as aggressive as I needed them to be. I thought he'd turn me out, but all I got was mediocre sex. Was I disappointed? A little, but I knew this thing between me and Drew was going nowhere. This was just a one-night fuck. A lazy fuck that knocked him out cold, and left me wide awake, staring at the walls at three in the morning.

By five o'clock in the morning, I'd gotten a little sleep and was sprawled out on the bed. I heard a hissing sound that caused me to quickly jump up and cover my breasts with the pillow. As I focused my eyes, I saw Jeff spraying Febreze in the air.

"Look, I don't know what you did in here last night, but whatever done died ain't going to heaven, smelling like that. What in the name of Jesus is going on in here?"

I rolled my eyes at Jeff. I'd put any amount of money on it that he knew exactly what had happened in here last night. I was surprised to see that Drew was gone. I must've been knocked out when he left.

"Jeff, you know what went on in here last night, so stop pretending."

"You damn right I know, Miss I'm So Over Men. That hunk of chocolate was more man than I've seen in a long time, but that nigga need to get them feet together. Those socks got this whole room fungy. Not funky, but fungy. He left his socks and I had to go wash them."

"I'm sure he'll appreciate that, but don't be so sure about all that hunk of chocolate being good. It was just okay. I was hoping for something better for sure."

"See, that's why I don't judge a book by its cover. The fine ones fail you every time. And the ugliest mofo you can find is the one who can shut that shit down and have you somewhere sucking your own thumb."

"I've never had anything that good. Neva, eva, eva."

"I would've sworn Brent was that good, especially by the way you acted in the past."

Jeff did it again. I got tired of hearing about it. Bringing up my past with Brent was starting to piss me off.

"I gotta say this, Jeff, and I do not mean any harm. Stop throwing that shit in my face, okay? I know what I did and I've taken responsibility for everything. I don't need you to keep reminding me how foolish I was. I got it. I know it, and I'm trying my best to do better. I'm so glad you never made any mistakes in your relationships. That you never did anything foolish that you regret. But most people do make mistakes and they do things that may be out of character, especially when they love somebody. I thought I was in love. Now I know better, but must I be criticized for that shit for the rest of my life?"

I got up and went into the bathroom. After I slammed the door, I sat on the toilet, thinking. Jeff knocked, but I didn't say anything.

"Look, Sweet Pea, you're right. You know I joke around a lot, but sometimes I go too far. I'mma stop, okay? It's fine to call me out on my shit, because people have to do that sometimes. But just so you know, if you ever raise your voice at me like that again, I'mma beat yo bony ass. I can fight, bitch, and I promise you, you won't be as pretty as you are when I get done with you. Get some rest and I'll check in later. Love you, Boo."

I smiled and covered my face with my hands. No matter what, Jeff was too sweet. He knew certain things needed to be said. The fact that he understood it meant more to me than he would ever know.

CHAPTER TWENTY-TWO

BRENT CARSON

My job at Hazelwood High was a wrap. I was bored as ever at home, and there was only so much of Kendal I could take. That's why she had her own place, and I had mine. I intended to keep it that way, but money was starting to get a little funny. Whenever that had happened in the past, I was able to dig in my savings or ask the long line of women I'd dated if I could borrow some money. I never had any issues before, but now that I was trying to limit the women in my circle, things had gotten a little tight.

Kendal wasn't much help at all. At first, I told her she would never have to work and I would take care of her. She took advantage of that. All she did, all day long was chat with her friends on social media, watch reality TV shows, shop and order takeout food. Now that things had changed, she had to step it up. I mean really step it up and get us the kind of money we needed to survive. I decided to run some of my ideas by her, just to see where her head was at. We were at the dinner table, eating Applebee's that was recently delivered.

"All I'm saying is things are going to get tight. We need to come up with a plan and execute it."

She licked the sauce from her finger then wiped it with a napkin. "What kind of plan, Brent? Like, I go work somewhere at a fast-food joint or start bagging groceries? Is that what you want me to do?"

"You don't have to inject your sarcastic bullshit into the conversation. I'm just trying to see if we can come up with a strategic plan to get some money or find out if you have any suggestions."

She took a hit from the blunt she smoked, then whistled smoke in the air. "I have some suggestions. What about you keep on getting money from your tricks like you've been doing? How about you go get another job that doesn't require you to be around young women and girls who keep throwing their pussies at you? Maybe you can become a trash man or a DoorDash driver. I hear they make a lot of money, and those ideas are just a start."

This was the downside of dealing with immature bitches. They were too incompetent to come up with real solutions, and what kind of man wanted to sit at the dinner table eating Applebee's all fucking week? Kendal had forgotten who I was. I needed to remind her, and do it quick because she was starting to be a replica of her mother. I looked at her pitiful ass from across the table and sucked my teeth.

"You're so fucking stupid. I keep hoping you'll woman up and be the young lady I had hoped, but you fail me every single time. You can take all of those suggestions and shove them up your ass. After you do that, you're going to give much consideration to getting off your lazy butt, and going to make us some money. Niggas out here paying hundreds of dollars for blowjobs. Rich white men just want to feel your pussy for thousands. Athletes and politicians paying big dollars to dick down young women like you, for five fucking minutes, and yo ass sitting over there on all that good pussy broke. I suggest you get more creative than bagging groceries or working at fast food joints. If your future is with me, you need to have bigger goals than that."

Kendal was fuming. She lifted her plate of sticky hot wings and threw it at my face. Threw it so hard that the plate cracked and hit the floor. By then, I had already jumped up from the table and snatched her ass up. I drug her over to the sink and put her whole head underneath the faucet. After turning the hot water pressure on high, I held her head so she wouldn't move. She could definitely scream though. And that she was.

"Cool the fuck off," I yelled. "Cool yo ass down and stop doing stupid shit to provoke me!"

I drenched her ass, and when she agreed to straighten the hell up, I turned the water to cold. I released her head and backed away from her. She hurried to stand up, and when she did, her long hair and face was dripping with water. It was all on her clothes and a puddle grew by her feet. She wiped her face while staring at me with an evil gaze.

"I know yo tough ass ain't crying, are you?" I said. "Not you. Not the one who be talking mad shit but can't back it up."

"I . . . I'm sorry," she said, sniffling. "I was wrong."

I didn't hold back and I didn't feel sorry for her. "Fuck you," I said, then snatched my jacket from the chair. I slammed the door on my way out and went to go sit in the car. When I looked at my phone and saw a text message from Abby, I slammed my phone against the dash, almost cracking it.

YOUR TIME IS ALMOST UP. EVERY DAY COUNTS. ENJOY YOUR FREEDOM WHILE IT LASTS.

I deleted her message, and did something I hadn't done in a long time. I called Lajuanna. I needed her. I always needed her. She was the only woman who was able to help me when I'd found myself slipping like this. There was no doubt that I was slipping; I was about to hurt somebody. Lajuanna always pulled me back from the brink of losing myself. She straightened me up. She knew how to do it, and she always forgave me after I fucked up. I had done so many, many times before, but after months apart, she always came back to me.

"Hi Brent," she said in a soothing tone.

"You have no idea how good it feels to hear your voice. Are you busy?"

"A little. What's up?"

"I just wanted to holler at you. Going through some things, and whenever things get rough, you know I have to always seek my rock. Please don't take that the wrong way."

"It's not really a compliment to me. I don't know how else you want me to look at it."

"I just had to say it, because it's the truth. I miss you so much, and I know you get tired of me telling you how sorry I am. I don't know why I can't get myself together, but if you would consider giving us one more chance, you have my word things will be different this time."

I heard her sigh. "Brent, by now, I know your word doesn't mean one thing. And those apologies you keep dishing out, please save them for someone else. I'm just trying to find my peace over here. Why can't you let me be at peace, and if you're not going to do right, just leave me alone."

"This time, I promise. I will do right. Just don't give up on me. You can't give up completely on us, and all these years we've been together means something."

Lajuanna said she'd think about it and would be here in a few weeks so we could talk. The fact that she was considering getting back with me gave me hope. I was happy about that for sure. So happy that I wanted to go back inside and tell Kendal Daddy was feeling better. Then, I changed my mind. Instead, I drove to a little hole in the wall bar on Broadway and had myself a few drinks. As I was tossing back my third drink, someone tapped my shoulder. It was a short man who looked very familiar to me. I'd definitely seen him before, and then I realized he was Karla's husband.

"Let's get something straight," he said, blowing his alcoholic breath on me. He was about ten . . . maybe even fifteen years older than I was, and was chubby as fuck. "I didn't have no problems with you creeping with my wife, until my money got involved. She finally admitted what she'd done with the money and I told her she needed to do whaaaaaatever to get it back. It appears that her attempts have been unsuccessful. I'm here to collect. You need to pay up right now."

Ignoring this clown, I turned in my seat, tossed back more alcohol and looked straight ahead. When he swung on me, I ducked and watched him fall flat on his face. That's when I stood up, paid for my drinks and looked down at him.

"Tell Karla that when the fifteenth of the following month gets here, I'll see what I can do about the money. As for me and you, I would fuck you up for swinging on me, but since her pussy wasn't good enough for me to fight you over it, I won't. Have a nice evening, sir."

I left the bar, realizing that the heat was starting to rise, maybe even explode. Lajuanna needed to make up her mind quick. If things worked out for us, in a few more weeks I'd be able to move away with her and leave all of this bullshit behind.

CHAPTER TWENTY-THREE

Something in my gut told me to make some moves—fast. I needed to see Kendal, again, and try my best to get through to her. This time, I had to take the hard punches. I had to take the insults and deal with the fact that I had not been there for my child like she needed me to. It wasn't too late to change things around. I wasn't going to give up. I couldn't give up, and as long as there was breath in me, I had to do whatever I could to fix this and get Kendal away from Brent.

This time it was almost one o'clock in the afternoon when I knocked on Kendal's door. There was no answer, but I continued to knock.

"Kendal, I already know you're in there. Where else are you going to go? All you do is stay cooped up in there, waiting for Brent to show up. He's not coming today. You know why? Because he's with his other woman. With his other women, more like it. With girls like you who he ain't got no business being with. You know this Kendal. I know you know this, and hate me all you want to, but you know this is not right."

I knew she could hear me. I knew she'd heard every single word I'd said. It wasn't until I told her I wasn't going to leave until she left with me, when she finally swung the door open.

"I wouldn't dare go anywhere with you," she hissed.

There was a red mark on the side of her face. Her hair was in a ponytail and I could clearly see she'd been slapped or punched. Yet again, I was tore up inside. I begged her to come with me, but she refused.

"Mama, what don't you understand? Why is this so hard for you to comprehend?"

She walked away from the door and I went inside. I closed the door behind me and reached out for her hand.

"I can't go because you're my child and I love you. I hate what I allowed to happen to you and I'm so very sorry. Let's go figure this out together. Deep down, I know you're not happy here. I know you aren't and you can lie to me all you want to."

She opened the fridge, popped open a can of soda and looked at me like she didn't even care. I started to think this wasn't the same little girl I had raised. This wasn't the little baby I had rocked in my arms. No, this wasn't the little girl I had spoiled rotten, and who I had loved since the day she was born. Standing before me was Brent's girlfriend. That's all she desired to be. I wanted her to be so much more than that.

"Every time I see you, I realize more and more how messed up you are," she said. "I never said you didn't love me, but what I'm saying to you is leave me alone and let me live my own life. If that life happens to be with Brent, so be it. I think you're jealous, more than you are anything else. You wish that you lived here, not me. That's what this is all about, for real. Go ahead and be honest. Tell the truth."

She walked away and went into the bedroom. I followed; it was so hurtful being there. Photos of the two of them together were on the nightstand. Some of his shoes were lined against the wall. There was a big poster of them on the closet door, and numerous bottles of his cologne were on the dresser. The bed was messy, but Kendal plopped on it. She reached for something else on the nightstand and held it in her hand. I didn't see what it was, until she widened her hand.

"Come check it out, Mama. We're getting married. Brent proposed to me yesterday and we're about to be husband and wife. I assume you won't be at the wedding, but feel free to give me your blessings while you're here. It's the least you can do, especially if your main goal is to see me happy."

I promised myself that I wouldn't lose it, but I was five seconds away from dragging her out of here. Things were about to turn ugly. There was nothing I could say or do to stop that from happening. I stepped forward and grabbed her arm.

"I'm done talking," I said. "Let's go, now. There ain't no way in hell you're going to marry his ass!"

Kendal snatched away from me. She shoved me back and elbowed me in the stomach. I grabbed it, and by the time I stepped forward to go after her again, she stood next to the bed with a gun cocked sideways in her hand. I knew things would get serious. Just not this serious. I inched back with my hands in the air, pausing right near the door.

"Kendal, what are you doing?" Tears rolled down my face. "Don't do anything stupid and please don't do anything you'll regret."

She remained cold as ice. I hadn't a clue who the person with the gun was and never in my wildest dream did I think it would come down to this.

"No regrets, Mama. None and you leave me no choice because you refuse to leave me and Brent alone."

I was so focused in on her that I didn't even notice Brent standing in the doorway. When Kendal's eyes shifted, mine did too. That's when I saw him standing there suited up in a navy suit, leather loafers and a crisp white shirt like he was the motherfucking man.

"Shoot her, baby," he ordered Kendal to do. "Get rid of her and let's be done with this."

I doubted that Kendal would listen to him, but I was so wrong. Her finger squeezed the trigger, and as a bullet whizzed toward me, I ducked and fell to the floor. Kendal actually laughed. She. Laughed. She pulled the trigger again, but purposely tried to miss me. I rolled around as the bullet went into the floor next to me.

"Stop this!" I fearfully cried out. I knew I was about to die, but never did I think it would be by my daughter's own hands.

"She's right, stop this," Brent said in a calm tone. "I would never want you to have to live with murdering your own mother. That's for me to do, not you."

Brent tossed his jacket aside and reached behind him. When I saw the gun, I tried to run like hell, but there was no place to run to. It was over for me. I was done and there wasn't a damn thing I could do about it.

"Do what you have to do then," Kendal said.

"I will," he replied. That's when the four loud booming sounds blasted off and made my ears ring like a loud bell that wouldn't stop chiming. My whole body was numb. I was frozen in time, and when I saw gashing big holes in my baby's chest, I opened my mouth wide. What seemed like slow motion, I shouted "noooooooooooo" and hurried to my feet. Barely able to stand, I stumbled over to where Kendal was and tried to catch her body before it dropped. It had already hit the floor. I grabbed her and laid her across my legs. Thick blood filled her mouth, but I covered it with mine, trying to save her.

"Come on baby," I cried out and kept pumping my air into her mouth. "Breathe Kendal, Breatheeeeeeeee!!

I got nothing. Nothing at all. Her eyes were locked wide open. She stared at me without a single blink.

"God damn you!" I shouted while rocking my sweet baby in my arms. All of her blood stained my clothes. I was drenched with her fucking blood and that bastard snatched up the ring and left. He was gone. I slowly removed Kendal from my lap and laid her on her back. My hands trembled over her chest wounds, and I continued planting soft kisses all over her face.

"I know you see me. I know you feel me. I know you know how much mommy loves you, and I'm so damn sorry for this. Baby I am sorry!"

I heard the police sirens in the distance and knew I had to go. I had to leave my baby, again, but this time for a good reason. Brent was a dead man, and for the very last time, I touched the side of Kendal's face.

"Mommy will see you soon, okay? No more worries and—"

I choked up as I used my fingers to close her eyelids. I kissed her one more time, just one more time again. After that, I opened the bedroom window, kicked out the screen and made my way through it. I could see the police cars coming, so I hid behind several bushes and fell several times from my legs being so weak. A few people saw me, but they didn't say a word. I hopped a fence, and in broad daylight, I crossed a busy street with blood-stained clothes and a mind that was completely gone. Several cars almost hit me. I heard numerous horns blowing and jumped out of the way to avoid being hit. Before I knew it, numerous police cars started to circle me. I kept looking for somewhere to run, but there was nowhere to go. My heart pounded against my chest and I eased my hands up high.

"Get down on the ground!" An officer shouted as he aimed his gun at me. They all had their weapons aimed at me, but my eyes shifted to the one that mattered the most. Officer Eric Wayne.

"Put your hands up high and lay down on the ground! Now, Abby, and don't do anything stupid! It's over!" he roared. "Over!"

It wasn't over, until I said it was over. I guess he didn't know that, at this point, I didn't give a damn about dying. I mean mugged his fake ass and looked around at all the people standing around, glaring at me like I was the crazy one. Like I was the one who had done something so wrong that it deserved all of this.

Who in the hell were they to stand there and judge me? To look at me like I was pathetic and jail or death was my only resolution. Maybe for Brent, but surely not for me. I scanned my surroundings and that's when I spotted him. He was standing there with a sly grin on his face. A grin that made my blood boil and caused me to stand, instead of kneel down. As I attempted to sprint forward, that's when I heard a thunderous boom. My body hit the concrete pavement, and then there was silence.

CHAPTER TWENTY-FOUR

I lay there and couldn't move. I didn't know if I was dead or alive, but there was a bright, blinding light coming from somewhere. A metal ceiling fan blew on me from above. I kept opening and closing my eyes, trying to focus. Each time I was able to open my eyes, my head started throbbing. There was a pain, unlike any pain I had ever experienced before. The last thing I remembered was being tased. It hurt and the painful tingling sensation felt like bolts of electricity rushing through my body. My mouth was real dry and my whole body was freezing cold. I was almost naked. All I had on was a pair of panties. A thin white sheet was over me and the gurney I was on was next to a concrete wall. I shifted my head from side-to-side, and when I turned to the right side again, that was when I saw Eric. Officer Eric Wayne, sitting in a chair next to me, proudly wearing his police uniform. One of his legs was crossed over the other. He sat as if he didn't have a care in the world, with a cigarette dangling from the corner of his mouth. He struck a match, and used the fiery flame to light the tip. After several puffs from the cigarette, he released smoke into the air. He kept staring at me. His lips, however, remained sealed. I shifted my head to the side, immediately thinking about Kendal. I hoped and prayed all of this was a dream and I was just now waking up. That somehow I had never escaped from jail and everything resorted back to the way it was when I was locked up. After all, none of this would've happened, if I would've been willing to pay for my crimes.

But this was real. It was a new day; a day that I didn't want to come. Brent had been victorious and had taken my daughter down with me. Eric was there for the celebration and only lord knows who else. I was done. This was over, and I assumed I'd be heading back to jail, soon, to finish my sentence—and more. If not that, Eric was going to kill me.

A tear seeped from the corner of my eye, and when I attempted to sit up, I couldn't. My wrists were tied to the rails. I figured they would be, but my legs were free. I stretched them and wiggled my toes to be sure none of them had been cut off. Yeah, Eric was dirty like that. He didn't give a shit about anything. He proved that a long time ago, and time and time again when he refused to do anything about Brent. Friend or no friend, Eric let Brent get away with it all. I thought he'd one day man up, but as I lay there, I realized he'd had Brent's back all along.

"Where's my daughter?" My head faced the wall. I just couldn't face him again. "Where am I and how long have I been here?"

"Three interesting questions and here are the short answers. Your daughter is buried, thanks to Jeff. You've been here for a few days, and it doesn't matter where you are."

I tried to process what little he'd said. Kendal buried. Jeff. A few days and he wasn't going to say where I was.

There was only one other question to ask him. "Why am I still alive? Go ahead and kill me. I'm not going back to that jail, and if I do, it won't be for long."

"I really don't care what you do to yourself, but this ain't over until I say it is. I enjoy watching you suffer like this, Abby. You played your little game and all of it backfired. Let this be a lesson to you. Don't fuck with me or else you will lose. For me, killing you would be too easy. After all you've done, nah, let's wait. You have a few visitors coming soon, and if we're going to do this again, we must do it right this time."

I didn't know what the hell he was talking about. I just lay there for a few minutes and didn't say anything. Then, a few more minutes later, I shifted my head to look at him. I wanted to slap that smirk right off his face. If I could punch him, it surely would've made me feel good. But none of that would've been enough to fully satisfy me. I wanted Brent. I regretted not killing that bastard when I'd had the chance. Time and time again, that gun was in my purse. I could've just ended it. But no, I fucked around, kept making excuses, kept feeling bad and was so worried about going back to jail. But . . . look at me now. I was screwed. Fucked, to be honest, and this loser was in control. Well, that's what I thought, until I actually heard Brent's voice.

"Sorry it took me so long to get here today," Brent said. "Traffic was a mutha and Lajuanna was taking all day at the airport."

"Don't sweat it," Eric said. "Look who's finally awake over there."

I closed my eyes to avoid looking at him. If there was a word that surpassed hate, somebody needed to tell me what it was. My whole body shut down as he came over to where I was, taunting me with a sly-ass grin on his face.

"Just so you know," he said, moving his face close to mine. He rubbed his finger along the top of my forehead. "I've been here every day checking on you. I had to see you and make sure you were okay. I know you're upset about Kendal, but I feared she was about to slip and betray me. Plus, she was getting out of hand and didn't want to work. She was a fucking brat who was starting to remind me too much of you. A brat that was standing in the way of my happiness. There were no other options, especially since I'd been making plans to reconcile with Lajuanna. I purchased her a new ring and everything. Too bad your dumb daughter thought it was for her."

He was masterful at hurting me. Man did his words sting. Since he decided to get this close to me, I gathered spit in my mouth, once again, and made sure it sprinkled all over his face. This time, he laughed and wiped his face with his hand.

"You are getting real good with that spit, but at this point, it don't even matter. If that's all you got, cool. It's whatever, baby. I get to watch you suffer and that's good enough for me."

He leaned in and put his lips over mine. He kept pecking my lips, and each time I felt them, I chomped down with my teeth, trying to bite the shit out of him.

"Damn, you taking bites at me like a baby shark." He laughed and then turned to look at Eric. "She's a feisty ass something. Was she this feisty when she was with you?"

"All day, every day," Eric said. "She had a very hard time controlling herself."

Brent looked at me, shaking his head. "You're such a slut. There you were claiming to love me so much, yet screwing around with him. Had you only known you were being set up. We set you up good, baby, and we had to do it, just so we could all have the peace of mind we deserved."

"Yes, we all need that," I heard a female say. When Brent swung around, that's when I saw Lajuanna. She still looked the same and much of her hair was shaved off. It was blonde, and she was dressed in camouflage pants and an olive green t-shirt. Her rubber boots had one hell of a shine on them. I never, ever understood why she stood by Brent and his foolishness for so long. I guess like so many of us, she was brainwashed and hooked on him too.

"What's this about," Brent said with a twisted face.

I didn't realize what he'd meant, until he moved further out of the way and I saw Lajuanna holding a small pistol in her hand. Eric was still sitting in the chair, chilling, as if he wasn't bothered at all.

"What this is about is you," Lajuanna said, tearfully. "All about you, baby. All about your lies, manipulation, cheating, killing and everything else you've done. When does it stop, Brent? Why didn't you ever stop, and how many people have to get hurt until you realize enough is enough?"

Brent stood speechless in disbelief. So was I. I lay there holding my breath, hoping and praying this wouldn't end like it did the last time we were all together. Last time, I went to jail. I thought Brent was dead, but he wasn't. They played me good, and

I hoped like hell this wasn't another game they were playing with me.

"Are you fucking serious?" Brent barked with spit flying from his mouth. His eyes shifted from Lajuanna to Eric.

"It appears that she's real serious," Eric said, and then he looked at Lajuanna. "Are you serious? If so, tell the man how serious you really are."

"Dead serious, Brent. It's over, baby. I'm sorry, but this is over. You've done enough. You've hurt too many people, and I tried my best to love you. I gave you everything." Lajuanna got choked up, as tears trickled down her face. Her chin trembled as she spoke, and if she was acting, she did a damn good job at it. I, of all people, felt her pain. "Turn yourself in and surrender right now. You gotta do the time and you must pay for what you've done."

I could feel sweat rolling off my entire body. I couldn't believe this was happening. Was this it? Was Brent really getting ready to go to jail? He took a few steps towards Lajuanna, but Eric finally stood and stopped him. He stood between Lajuanna and Brent, with his hand on Brent's chest.

"Like she said, it's over man. Turn around, put your hands behind your back, because I'm placing you under arrest."

"You've got to be fucking kidding me. Am I being punked or something? Stop playing this game with me. This is not funny. Where in the hell are the cameras at?"

"You know where the cameras were, Brent," Lajuanna said. "The cameras were just where you left them. In our house when you filmed those underage girls you had sex with. In my house, while I was away, fighting for my country and loving your dirty drawers. How could you be so fucking cruel to me, and stupid at the same time?"

Brent's mouth was wide. I think reality was starting to set in for him, and for me. Thing is, he wasn't going down without a fight. He tried to rush Eric, but he punched Brent so hard that it sent him flying on top of me. Lord knows I wanted a piece of him, but my hands were still tied. I grunted and tried to use my body to push him off of me. By that time, Eric was already right there. Him and Brent tussled. Eric managed to quickly wrestle Brent on his stomach, and as he continued to lay over me, his hands were tightened behind his back. Heavy breaths escaped from Brent's bloody mouth; he looked at me with the meanest mug I had ever seen on his face.

"Fool, you are going to pay for this," Brent grunted while speaking to Eric. He wasn't fazed one bit. He held Brent down, proving to him who, indeed, now had the upper hand. That's when a smirk appeared on my face.

"Don't get too happy," Brent said while keeping his eyes on me. "Bitch, this ain't over yet. Just wait and see."

Eric cuffed him, and the second he stood him up, two shots rang out.

"Yes it is," Lajuanna said, as Brent fell forward and landed on top of me again. "Yes it is over. It's over now."

She dropped the pistol and it hit the floor. Eric released Brent, and his lifeless body slipped off mine and hit the floor, too. The loud thud caused me to jump. So did the sound of Eric's loud voice.

"Why in the fuck did you do that? I told you to let me arrest him and take him in! What in the hell were you thinking! That's not how I do things. I should arrest you, too."

"Do whatever, Eric." Lajuanna looked defeated as she locked her eyes on Brent, crying her heart out. It never, ever dawned on me how much she had actually been through with him. My situation with him was enough. But, hell, there were so many other women involved with him, and she was his . . . wife. A wife who had endured it all.

Eric scratched his head while gazing at Brent on the floor. A pool of blood ran from underneath him. He surely looked dead to me. Eric placed his hands behind his head, swung around and closed his eyes like he was in deep thought. When he opened them, he looked at me.

"Come on, let's go," he said. He started to remove the ropes from my wrists.

"Go where?" I asked.

"You're going back to jail. Brent deserved what he got and you do too. You have to finish your time, Abby. You must, indeed, finish your time in jail."

I was disappointed to hear that, but whatever. I needed to heal from all of this, and maybe jail was the place to do it. At this point, I simply didn't care anymore. Like Lajuanna, I felt defeated and broken as well.

"No," Lajuanna said. "Let her go, Eric. She's been through enough, and this isn't about you being some kind of hero, because you're not."

"I'm not letting her go," Eric fussed. "Hell no, and I'm not trying to be nobody's damn hero. This woman needs to be in jail. We needed her here to trick Brent, and you told me I would be able to take her to jail, once all of this was finished. There's no way I'd be able to explain her being on the loose, again."

"Let her go!" Lajuanna shouted. "I'm sure you'll figure it all out and come up with something clever. If you don't, we're all going down in here together."

I wasn't sure what she meant by that, but her words caused her and Eric to look at the pistol on the floor. His eyes then shifted to me. He pondered for a while; I assumed he was trying to figure out what he could say or do, if he released me.

"Fuck," he said, as he turned away from me and cut his eyes at Lajuanna. "We had a deal."

"Deal or no deal," she said. "I helped you a lot. You need to help me and let her go. Now Eric."

Eric frowned as he turned to me again. His words were stern. "I don't want you in my city. Leave St. Louis for good. Don't you ever come back, and I never want to see your face again. Got it?"

I didn't say a word. I swallowed the lump in my throat and sat up when he removed the other rope from my hand. Since I didn't have on any clothes, he gave me his jacket and ordered me to find the best way out of there. I wanted to thank the bastard, but I couldn't. Wanted to say thanks to Lajuanna, but I was too ashamed to face her. Instead, I made my way to the door, but stopped before I could reach it. I turned and looked at the pistol on the ground. It was still there. I rushed over to it, because I had to be sure that Brent was dead. That this was no game and he wouldn't show up later, saying surprise. I needed this to be over, and since I didn't get a chance to shoot him myself, this would give me a little satisfaction I needed. I picked up the pistol. Thinking I was going to shoot him, Eric grabbed his gun and aimed it at me. Lajuanna moved out of the way. I shot the pistol, two more times. One in Brent's head, one in his heart. His body jerked. More blood seeped from him. I kicked him with the tip of my foot, and as his body shifted, that's when I knew, for a fact, Brent Carson was dead. I dropped the gun, glanced at Eric one last time, and then I left.

CHAPTER TWENTY-FIVE

LAJUANNA CARSON

Dressed in a black, single-breasted pantsuit and Christian Louboutin heels, I was clean as ever. My shaved blonde hair was sharply lined, and no one could see my slanted brown eyes behind the dark shades I wore. With my legs crossed, while sitting on the front pew of the church, I listened to the choir sing "Amazing Grace." I tuned out the numerous cries that echoed throughout the sanctuary, and there were plenty of people sniffling and singing aloud around me. Many people had their eyes locked on me. They were waiting for me to scream and shout, run up and down the aisles or even fall to my knees in front of Brent's casket. There would be none of that, simply because I wasn't feeling the pain many of the people in this church felt. What I felt was relief. Only God knew what Brent had put me through, and for twenty-something years, I pretended that everything was fine. I turned my back when I knew shit wasn't right. Smiled in front of our friends and family, when I simply wanted to cry. Put up with his lies and cheating, and took him back every single time. Even when he beat my ass until my face was black-and-blue, I blamed myself and accepted his apologies. It was me who emboldened

Brent—gave him power and made him feel like if he could do all of this to me, he could go out there and do other women the same damn way.

For twenty-something years, I left and came back. I kept telling myself that things would get better and Brent would, eventually, grow into the man I had always hoped he would be. But as I stayed away fighting for my country, he got worse. The last straw was when Toya had reached out to me. What she'd told me caused me to dig deeper and find out more about the man I'd called my husband. What I'd found out troubled me in so many ways. The videos he'd taken of him having sex with women and young girls who were Toya's age, it crushed me. Tore me up, and when I'd found out about Abby's daughter, Kendal, I was devastated. I wanted to kill myself to alleviate my pain. Instead, I just left. Walked for the fourth or fifth time in our marriage, and felt responsible for some of his actions because I hadn't done enough to examine the monster I'd been married to.

By the time Eric had gotten in touch with me, I was ready to spill my guts to him. I wanted to, and he and I came up with a plan to shut Brent down for good. What Eric didn't know was how much I despised Brent. How much I'd hated him, and how if he was going to die, it wouldn't be by nobody else's hands, but mine. Not Abby's, Toya's, Kendal's, Karla's . . . but mine. While they had experienced Brent's wrath for months, or maybe even a few years, I'd been the one who had experienced it for twenty-something-fucking years.

So now, today, everybody wanted to sit around me weeping. Brent's family was here, clowning. Toya was in the far back, crying her heart out. Karla was to my left, wiping her eyes as if she'd really lost something. Shanelle sobbed uncontrollably, and numerous women I'd seen in some of the photos, hooted and hollered like it was the end of the world.

Me, however, I sat there in silence, looking straight ahead. I was now listening to one of Brent's coworkers go on and on about what a great guy he was.

"Like, I could count on Mr. Carson for anything," the tall white man said. "He was the counselor everybody loved and could go to for anything. We are truly going to miss him. Our entire school is in mourning, and without Mr. Carson around, things will never, ever be the same."

Many people clapped and agreed. Several other people got up to express themselves as well, and right after the last woman wrapped up her thoughts, I went to the podium to speak. I removed my shades and looked throughout the sanctuary where every last seat was filled. Some people even stood up in the back, eyeing me and waiting for my final words. Of course, I thanked everyone for coming, and then I continued on with my prepared remarks.

"My dear husband," I said, looking at the gold colored casket I'd picked out for him. "In front of all of these people, I can honestly say that you ain't shit, she wasn't ever shit, and some of the women in here crying over you ain't shit either. Now that you're gone, may they all get a damn life and may you, my sorry-ass husband, now rest in hell."

"Damn," the piano player said, after hitting one dreadful note on the piano. I could see the shocked looks on so many faces. Some people got up and walked out.

"What did she say?" I heard another lady behind me ask.

"God don't like ugly," the pastor roared.

"She said, what she said," someone else replied.

By that time, I had stepped away from the podium and didn't even look at Brent's casket as I proceeded to parade down the main aisle and leave. The whispers got louder and louder, but I didn't care.

"Now, she was wrong for that."

"What did he do?"

"He really wasn't shit, though."

I pushed the double doors to the church open and left feeling free. As soon as I stepped down from the first step, I felt someone grab my arm. My head shifted to the right, and that's when I saw another woman in black with a black veil covering her face. It was Abby.

"I just wanted to tell you that I'm so sorry for hurting you. Thank you for everything, and I truly mean that from the bottom of my heart. I'm here because I needed to know, for a fact, that all of this was real and it's finally over."

All I did was nod and smile. I strutted to the limousine, got inside and told the driver to drive off. As he did, behind the tinted windows my eyes stayed connected with Abby's. Eric and I wanted to use her help to bring Brent down, but she was too unstable. She would've messed up everything, that's why I told Eric to tie her up that day and do whatever to make her believe he was on Brent's side, not hers. Along with all the evidence I'd given him, Eric worked tirelessly at getting Brent to confess. After Eric had spoken to Toya, too, that was his breaking point. He'd thought arresting Brent was the solution, but that wasn't enough for me. I also knew that if I hadn't killed him, Abby would've found some way to get to him first. We were both mentally drained and severely damaged. I guess there was only so much some women could take. Like me, Abby had suffered enough. I wished her all the best, and I hoped like hell that she'd never find herself involved with another man like Brent Carson again.

FROM AUTHOR, BRENDA HAMPTON

Hello, Readers! Well, it looks like I came out of retirement to write another novel and I hope you all enjoyed it. Some of you already know, based on one of Facebook posts, that I decided to write this novel because it gave me an opportunity to clear my mind during these very challenging times. I hope that reading allows you to do the same and relax. Let's all pray that our lives get back to normal soon. Much love to you all!

www.brendamhampton.com